9

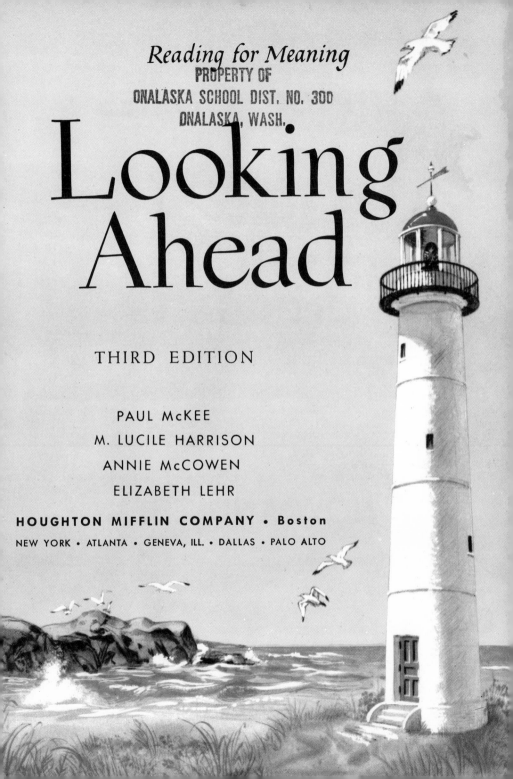

Reading for Meaning

Looking Ahead

THIRD EDITION

PAUL McKEE

M. LUCILE HARRISON

ANNIE McCOWEN

ELIZABETH LEHR

HOUGHTON MIFFLIN COMPANY • Boston

NEW YORK • ATLANTA • GENEVA, ILL. • DALLAS • PALO ALTO

~STORIES~

TIPTOP STORIES

OPEN GATES

NOW AND THEN

Tiptop Stories

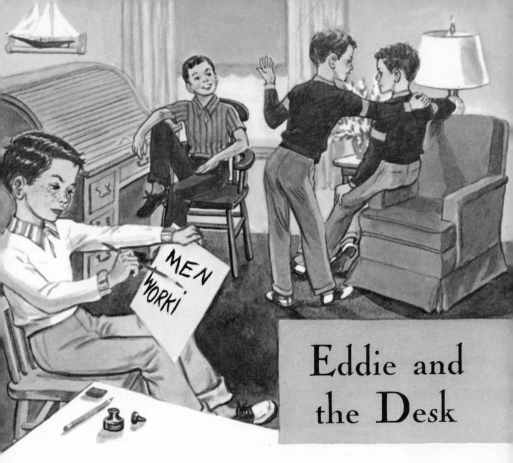

Eddie and the Desk

Eddie Wilson was seven years old. His three older brothers and their friends were always telling him he was too little to go around with them. But this never troubled Eddie. He went along just the same and somehow found a way to get in on nearly everything the older boys did.

But sometimes he had to think fast and work hard to do it.

Little Eddie liked animals. He was always bringing them home with him. Eddie found all the dogs and cats that didn't have any homes and all the little birds that fell out of their nests. Or maybe they found Eddie.

He kept all the old bones he could get for dogs. He was always asking at the fish store for fish heads for cats. His mother said that every cat in town could smell the fish heads and that they all lined up outside the Wilsons' back door.

Every dog seemed to know where Eddie lived and that he was always good for a bone. His father said Eddie must have put up a sign on the back door in dog and cat talk that said "Dinner Is Ready."

He also said Eddie would do better to bring home a horse to plow the garden. But none of this talk troubled Eddie. He thought his father and mother didn't really mean anything by what they said.

He thought the cat and dog sign might be a good thing. Eddie liked signs. Every time he saw one he went home and made one just like it.

His bedroom was filled with signs that he had made. When you opened Eddie's door you read, *Stop, Look, and Listen; Slow, Bridge Up; One Way Street; Do Not Park Here; Picnic Here, But Put Your Fire Out When You Leave.*

Eddie also liked to bring home all kinds of things that other people had thrown away. When housecleaning time came around, Eddie could hardly stay in school. He was afraid he might miss something that was being put out to be burned.

He had a place downstairs where he kept all these old things. Some day he was going to make a truck or a tractor out of them. He had pieces of rope, pieces of old pipe, broken locks, wire springs, an old wagon that needed paint, and even an old cowbell.

When Eddie left the house, nobody could guess what he might bring back with him. Eddie didn't care how big the thing was, or how he might puff over it. He always found some way to get it home. His mother often said that nothing he did would surprise her.

8

It didn't surprise her when Eddie came home with some strong paper boxes with handles and said they were just the right size to hold three by seven cards.

And it didn't surprise her when he turned his room into his office and kept his boxes there. But the day came when she was more than surprised.

One night when they were all at home in the kitchen eating sandwiches and drinking cocoa, Father said he believed he would buy a new desk. "May I have the old one, Father?" asked Eddie.

"Nothing doing!" said his brother Rudy. "I'm the oldest. I'm the one who needs it."

"No, no," shouted his brothers Joe and Frank who were twins.

"We get it, don't we, Father?" Frank asked. "There are two of us."

"It was Grandfather's desk," said Joe.

"And we were named for him," said Frank.

"I should chop it up for the fireplace," said Father. "I can't find any place to buy wood. And there isn't so much as a piece of old board left that I can use. We'll want to use the fireplace until spring."

"Oh, Father," cried Rudy. "You won't burn up Grandfather's desk, will you?"

"I didn't say I would," said his father. "I said I should."

Eddie drank some more cocoa. "But you won't, will you?" he asked.

"No, I won't," said Father. "But I tell you what I will do. I'll give the old desk to whichever one of you boys brings home the most firewood."

"Oh, Father," said Rudy. "Where are we going to get any wood?"

"I don't know," cried Father. "But I have tried, and now you boys can try. How's that?"

"All right," said Rudy.

"All right," said the twins.

"All right," said Eddie.

Some time went by and no one had any wood for the fireplace. The older boys were doing so many other things they never thought about the wood. Eddie just hadn't found what he was looking for.

Then, one day when Eddie came home from school, he saw some men at work in the street on which the Wilsons lived. The men were putting in a new telephone post.

Eddie Gets Some Help

Eddie was pleased. He sat down on the other side of the street and watched. Once he called out, "Would you like some help?"

The man nearest Eddie looked up. "No, thanks," he said. "I think we can do it alone. You just stay where you are and rest."

Eddie watched the men handle the ropes and get the new post into place. Then he looked at the old post in the street.

"I surely would like to have that post," thought Eddie. "That post is about as good as they come."

The men were about ready to take the post away. "If you don't want that old post," said Eddie, "I would like to have it."

When Eddie said that, the men looked surprised. "Now what do you want with a telephone post?" the head man asked.

"Well, my father could use it," said Eddie. "We've had a hard time finding wood to burn in the fireplace."

"I'm afraid your father will have to look somewhere else," said the man.

"But my father said if I could get some wood for the fireplace, I could have Grandfather's desk," said Eddie.

"He did?" said one of the men. "Here, Son! Help yourself to Grandfather's desk."

"Oh, thanks," said Eddie. Then he added, "I live right up the street in that white house with the white fence. Could you help me carry it home?"

The men laughed. "Help you carry it home?" asked one. "Well, men, shall we help the big boy carry the little telephone post home?"

Three of the men took the big end of the post, two of them took the little end, and Eddie put his arm around the middle. Then they all went up the street, through the front gate, and put the post down beside the fence.

"Now do you want us to help you cut it up?" asked the men.

"Oh, no, that's all right," said Eddie. "My father will cut it up."

He sat down on the post. When Mrs. Wilson came home, she found Eddie there. "Eddie, where did you get that?" she cried.

"The telephone men gave it to me," said Eddie. "Now I'll get Grandfather's desk."

"I guess you will," laughed Mother.

When the other boys came home, they were surprised to see the telephone post, and when Father heard of how Eddie came home with it, his glasses fell right off into his dinner.

15

Eddie put a sign on his door on the day the desk was put into his room. It said, *Men Working.*

All the others, who were downstairs, could hear Eddie pushing and pulling things around. They knew what he was doing. He was working to get his office ready. Then after a while, there was no more noise from Eddie.

Mother went to his room and carefully opened the door. When she looked in, there was little Eddie with his head on Grandfather's desk, sound asleep. Standing on the desk and showing above his head was a sign which said, *Help Wanted.*

His mother called downstairs to his father. Father came upstairs. He took Eddie and laid him on his bed. His mother undressed him and pulled the covers over him. Through all of this Eddie stayed asleep.

As Mother left the room, she saw another sign. She put it on the bedpost at the head of Eddie's bed. It said, *Quiet Please.*

17

The Trolley Car Family

GEORGE

BILL

DICK

SALLY

Mr. Jefferson, the milkman, didn't mind working at night while other people slept. That was his job. But the thing that made him cross was that other people forgot that he was just going to bed as they were getting up.

Mr. Jefferson's house was quiet because he lived all alone. But the noisiest family in town lived next door. That was the Parker family. The Parkers were the noisiest when Mr. Jefferson was the sleepiest.

MR. JEFFERSON

MR. AND MRS. PARKER

Mr. Parker drove a trolley car. Each morning Mrs. Parker and the four little Parkers went out to see him off for the day. That was when they were the noisiest.

Early one summer morning Mr. Jefferson was feeling very cross and sleepy as he drove home. He hoped that the Parker Family would go off on a picnic since it was a fine day and the children were not in school. If they stayed at home, he would get no sleep.

He drove the milk wagon to the barn, put it away, and gave his horses, Whitey and Blacky, their breakfasts. Then he went to the house to get his own.

Mr. Jefferson was just ready to get to bed when he remembered he had not seen or heard the Parker family. He began to worry. Something must be the matter. It was already after the time Mr. Parker left each day in his trolley car.

He looked out the window. He listened. He didn't see or hear any of the Parkers.

"Something is the matter," said Mr. Jefferson. He hurried out of his house and over to the Parker house. He pushed the doorbell and listened.

Sally Parker came to the door.

"Hello," said Mr. Jefferson. "I didn't see or hear anybody. I came over to see if anything is the matter."

"How do," said Mrs. Parker, who had followed Sally to the door. "I know why you thought something was wrong. We are not often as quiet as we are today. Come in, Mr. Jefferson. Have a cup of coffee with us."

Mr. Jefferson followed Mrs. Parker into the kitchen. There was Mr. Parker at the kitchen table, holding a cup of coffee. He didn't smile. He just looked worried. The rest of the family sat around and looked worried too.

"How do," said Mr. Parker.

"It will be quieter for you pretty soon, Mr. Jefferson," said Mrs. Parker. "We are going to move."

"Move!" cried Mr. Jefferson. "Why?"

"Go ahead, Mother, and tell him what's the matter," said Mr. Parker.

"Well, you see, it's this way," said Mrs. Parker. "All the trolley cars in town are to be stopped. There will be new buses to take their places.

"If Father would drive a bus in the city, he could keep his job. But he won't, so he's out of a job. We'll have to move soon. We can't rent this house much longer. We need to keep what money we have."

"Where are you going to move to?" asked Mr. Jefferson.

"I wish I knew," said Mrs. Parker. "The trolley car company said that Mr. Parker could have a month's pay while he looks for a job. But Father didn't take it.

"He asked for his old trolley car in place of the month's pay. They gave him the trolley car.

"Now we don't know what to do with the trolley car, and we have no place to move to."

Just then Sally, who had been listening, said, "Why can't we live in the trolley car? Then we won't have to pay rent, and Father won't have to drive a bus."

At first no one said anything. Then Mrs. Parker began to smile.

"That might work out," she said. "But where could we move the trolley car to?"

"We could move it to the picnic grounds or some other place like that out of town," said Bill.

Everybody but Mr. Parker looked happier.

"There's no power line out that far any more," he said. "I can't drive the trolley car out there without power."

"That's where I can help," said Mr. Jefferson. "I have the power."

"What power?" asked Mr. Parker.

"Why," said Mr. Jefferson, "Whitey and Blacky. We can hitch them to the trolley car. They can pull it."

The picnic grounds were owned by the trolley car company. That very day Mr. Parker went to talk with the company about renting him some of the land.

The Parker children could hardly wait for him to come home again. When at last they saw him coming, they raced down the street to walk home with him.

They asked one question after another as they danced around him. But not one word would he say until Mrs. Parker, too, could hear what he had found out. He climbed the front steps and sat down on the porch.

"Now tell us the whole story," said Mrs. Parker who had come out on the porch to hear the news.

"All right," said Mr. Parker. "There's an old farm farther from town than the picnic grounds. The company owns that, too. We can rent it. There's no house on the land. It burned down, but there's a good barn."

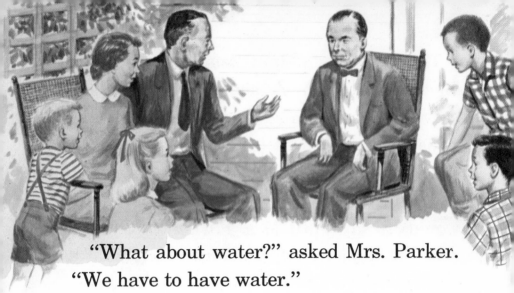

"What about water?" asked Mrs. Parker. "We have to have water."

"The company said that there was a good fresh spring on the land. It would give plenty of water for a large family. It used to be piped to the house."

Just then Mr. Jefferson came over and sat down on the porch. He wanted to hear the news, too.

Mr. Jefferson was sure that his horses could be hitched to the trolley car to get it out to the farm from the end of the power line.

"I'll try to get the horses right back," said Mr. Parker. "I know how busy you are."

"Why can't Mr. Jefferson take a vacation and come with us?" asked George.

"Oh, I never take vacations," said Mr. Jefferson. "I have to take the milk from the dairy to the people's houses."

"Now, Mr. Jefferson," said Mrs. Parker, "you should take a week's vacation. You work nights and sleep daytimes. You never get out in the sun. Come with us for a week. We'll have plenty of sun on the farm."

"Maybe I do need a vacation," said Mr. Jefferson. "Old Whitey and Blacky need one, too. They never get any sun."

"If you can stand these noisy children around, we would be pleased to have you for a week, a month, or as long as you like," said Mrs. Parker.

27

Mr. Jefferson almost smiled. "I haven't lived with a family for a long time," he said. "But I'd like to have a week's vacation on a farm. Are you sure I won't be in the way? I can get Mr. Brown at the dairy to take over my work for a week. I took his once."

At last the day came when the Parkers were to move and when Mr. Jefferson's vacation was to begin. Everybody was up with the sun. And everybody helped move all that the Parkers owned into the trolley car.

The children and Mrs. Parker got in and sat down. Mr. Parker turned on the power, and clanged the bell. Then the trolley car started off down the tracks.

28

Mr. Jefferson in his milk wagon drove Whitey and Blacky along the road beside the tracks.

Soon Bill left his seat to stand by his father. "May I clang the bell once?" he asked.

Mr. Parker laughed. "Go ahead," he said. "One more clang won't matter. People here may never again hear the clang of the bell on a trolley car going along these tracks."

The children were so excited that they had a hard time sitting in their seats. They called and waved to Mr. Jefferson as he drove along beside them.

In a short time, they came to the end of the power line. The tracks went farther, but there was no wire overhead to give them power. Now it was time to hitch Whitey and Blacky to the trolley car.

Mr. Jefferson and Mr. Parker hitched the milk wagon behind the trolley car. They hitched the two horses to the front of the car. Then Mr. Jefferson sat in Mr. Parker's seat to drive the horses.

The car moved on down the tracks. It made queer noises as it moved along because the tracks had not been used for a long time.

"I'll know the place when I see it," said Mr. Parker. "It has a big red barn. And across the road is a little yellow farmhouse with a big porch along one side."

"Bill and Sally, you're good at finding things," said Mrs. Parker. "You stand up front beside Mr. Jefferson and be our lookouts. It can't be much farther."

30

Mrs. Parker was right. They had not gone much farther when Bill called out, "There it is! Look up ahead!"

On one side of the road was the little yellow farmhouse with the big porch. On the other side was a green field. Far back from the road on that side was a red barn. And there the car tracks left the road and ran into the green field in front of the barn.

Mr. Jefferson stopped the horses. With one last loud noise, the trolley car stopped. Everyone got out and looked around.

Little Dick began to cry, "Dinner. I want my dinner."

"You poor little boy!" said Mrs. Parker. "You're hungry. I guess we're all hungry.

"You two big boys look around for firewood. Sally, you and I will open the box of food and get some milk for Dick."

Things began to move fast. The men had already unhitched the horses and tied them to a tree. The boys soon came back with their arms full of wood.

Mr. Parker started a fire. Near the fire, Mrs. Parker put a large pan of chicken and noodles that she had cooked early that morning. Then she made the coffee.

Before long, the Parker family and Mr. Jefferson sat down to a good dinner of chicken and noodles, fresh greens, and sandwiches. The grown-ups drank coffee, but the children had milk. There were oranges for the children also.

As soon as they had eaten, Mrs. Parker said, "We're all tired. We should go to bed as soon as we can."

Off went the Parker family to the beds Mrs. Parker had made across the seats of the trolley car. Mr. Jefferson had no problems. He slept on a bed he had made in the milk wagon.

Trolley Car Home

Early next morning, soon after the sun was up, Mr. Parker and the boys made a fire, and Mrs. Parker began to cook breakfast. Sally passed oranges for them to eat while the rest of the breakfast was cooking.

Soon Mrs. Parker had eggs and hot toast ready. The children had hot cocoa; the grown-ups had coffee.

"I haven't slept that well for a long time," said Mr. Jefferson, taking up his cup of coffee. "Anybody ought to sleep well in this good fresh air."

His mouth stretched into a wide smile. "Wouldn't the dairy company be surprised to see me now," he said. His smile became a laugh. "I feel like a new man already."

Suddenly everybody was laughing.

"That's a good way to start a day," said Mrs. Parker. "Our first problem is to get fresh water from that spring. You said it was piped to the house that burned down. Those pipes ought to be around somewhere."

The men found the pipes stored away in the barn. The boys went off to look for the spring. Before long, good cold spring water had been piped right to the trolley car.

"Now let's make a kitchen on one platform of the car so I won't have to cook over an open fire all summer," said Mrs. Parker. "We can burn wood in that small stove of ours."

34

The two men moved the stove to one end of the back platform. They ran the stove pipe out the top of one window.

"There!" said Mr. Jefferson. "That should be a good stove for a good cook. Now you ought to have a work table nearby. We can use some of the boards and nails we found in the barn. We can put it right on top of the motorman's box on this back platform."

"And Mother can sit on the motorman's stool," cried Sally.

While Mr. Jefferson was making the work table, Mrs. Parker was busy driving nails on both sides of the big window. They would hold her pans, cups, and other things a cook wants to have nearby.

Mr. Jefferson nailed another board up above the window for a shelf. "You ought to have a shelf to put canned goods on," he said.

"Oh, yes," said Mrs. Parker. "I'll need a shelf."

When the shelf was finished, Mrs. Parker sat down on the motorman's stool.

"This place begins to look homey already," she said. "I like a small kitchen, and I like this motorman's stool. I can sit down while I'm working, and I can put my hands on nearly everything in my kitchen."

She turned and looked at the other platform at the front of the car. "Let's take out some seats at the front of the car and put our living room furniture there. We can move the beds to the seats in the middle of the car. Then we'll have a living room, bedroom, and kitchen."

While they finished making the living room and putting the furniture there, Mr. Parker and the boys went to look over the barn.

On one side of the barn they found stalls for horses and stalls for cows. On the other side, they found many boxes nailed to the boards.

"Those are nests for chickens," said Mr. Parker. "We'll have to get some chickens so you can have fresh eggs for breakfast every day and chicken for Sunday dinner. Think of that!

"We'll put Whitey and Blacky in the stalls tonight," Mr. Parker went on. "Someday I'd like to have a barn with stalls full of horses and cows."

All week long, Mr. Jefferson and the Parker family were as busy as could be.

Mr. Parker found a good milk cow. Mrs. Parker got a nearby farmer to sell twelve hens and a rooster to her. Mr. Parker made roosts, and the boys filled the nests with fresh grass. Every day the children hurried to get the eggs that the hens had laid.

The children found some cherry trees and gathered cherries for Mrs. Parker to can. They found early apples and gathered some of them, too.

Every day Mrs. Parker was at work by the stove on the platform. She was always cooking, baking, or canning something. It was a busy place.

Mr. Jefferson made a small porch on the front of the trolley car. He made some outdoor furniture, too. But soon the time came when he had to think about getting back to his work for the dairy.

Exciting Times

"I'll have to begin sleeping in the daytime instead of at night," said Mr. Jefferson. "That's going to be hard."

The next morning Mr. Jefferson was up early, but the Parkers were up to say good-by to him. Not one of them wanted him to leave. They had found that he wasn't a cross man at all.

Mr. Parker was going into Springfield with Mr. Jefferson. He hoped to buy a bicycle he could ride when he needed to go to town.

He wanted to look for a job, too. He had
had a good week's vacation while Mr.
Jefferson had his. But now he would have
to earn something to pay the rent for the
land and to buy clothes and groceries.

The two men hitched the horses to the
milk wagon. Mr. Jefferson climbed into
the driver's seat, and Mr. Parker climbed
up beside him.

"Well, good-by," said Mr. Jefferson. "I've
had a fine vacation."

As the wagon turned the corner, Mrs.
Parker stepped up into her kitchen.

40

"I guess these dishes won't get washed without someone to help them," she said.

"Things will seem different without Mr. Jefferson," said Sally. All the others felt that way, too.

Late that night, Mr. Parker came riding home on a second-hand bicycle. He was hot, hungry, and tired.

"What kept you so long?" asked Mrs. Parker.

"Well, Mother, I went to talk to the trolley car company about a job," said Mr. Parker. "Now I have a new job. I'm going to drive the bus from Springfield to Five Corners. That line goes right by our door. I'll like that. I start work next week."

"Won't we have to move back to Springfield?" asked Mrs. Parker.

"No, we won't," said Mr. Parker. "We're going to stay right here. The children can go to school in Five Corners instead of Springfield. I can take them there on the bus in the morning and bring them back at night."

"With pay coming in every month, we won't have to worry about the money to pay the rent on the land. We can be sure of plenty to eat and clothes to wear, too," said Mrs. Parker.

"We'll also get another stove, when it begins to get cold," said Mr. Parker.

The next Monday morning, the Parker family stood by the side of the road and watched Mr. Parker as he rode off on his bicycle. This was the day he was to start the bus job.

42

Mrs. Parker and the children watched until Mr. Parker had turned the corner. Then they sat down on the grass to talk about the day's work.

Suddenly Bill jumped to his feet.

"Look!" he shouted. "Look up the road!"

A milk wagon with two horses was coming down the road. Everyone watched as it came nearer and nearer.

"That's Whitey and Blacky and Mr. Jefferson!" shouted George. "He's coming back to the farm!"

Mr. Jefferson drove right up to the excited children and got out of the wagon.

"I hope you've come for another vacation, Mr. Jefferson," cried Sally.

"No," said Mr. Jefferson, smiling. "Instead, I've come to stay. I couldn't stand it in my house in Springfield. It was too quiet. No noisy children! No squawking chickens! No rooster! No cows!"

"What about your job with the dairy?" asked Mrs. Parker.

"I gave it up," said Mr. Jefferson. "I found I could buy the little yellow farmhouse across the road. I'm going to start a dairy of my own. I've already bought Whitey and Blacky and the wagon."

"Goody, goody!" cried Sally. "We'll not let things get too quiet for you here."

"I'm sure of that," laughed Mr. Jefferson. "But where's Mr. Parker?"

Mrs. Parker told Mr. Jefferson about Mr. Parker's good luck in getting the bus line that would run right by their house.

44

"I saw a man riding a bicycle," said Mr. Jefferson, "but his head was down and I didn't see his face. That must have been Mr. Parker."

The rest of the summer was a busy time for everyone. Mr. Jefferson was busy finding good cows for his dairy farm. Mr. Parker was busy driving the bus. The boys had already started to gather wood for the winter. Sally looked after the chickens and little Dick. George and Bill helped Mr. Jefferson milk his cows. Mrs. Parker canned food for the winter.

45

When Mr. Jefferson, wearing his overalls and big hat, stood looking at his cows, no one could believe he had ever been cross.

"I haven't been so happy since I was a boy," he said almost every day.

"We've plenty to make us happy," said Mrs. Parker. "And to think it was Sally who told us we could live in the trolley car instead of a house!"

"It pays to listen to children," said Mr. Jefferson. "I'm glad you did."

The Bicycle Tree

Jody sat on the fence, looking at his peach tree. But Jody wasn't really seeing a peach tree. He was seeing a bicycle tree.

To be sure, there was no bicycle on the tree. Now the tree was just a peach tree covered with peach blossoms. But Jody knew that many of these blossoms would turn into peaches. He was thinking of the time when the tree would be covered with peaches instead of blossoms.

Jody thought he could turn the peaches into a bicycle without much trouble. That was why he thought he could see bicycles in his peach tree.

"If you do your part, I'll have that bicycle,"
Jody told the peach tree. The tree said
nothing at all. Like all the other peach
trees, it just stood there all dressed up in
its new spring blossoms.

"What are you doing, Jody?" asked
Sylvie. Sylvie was Jody's little sister. When
Jody was around, Sylvie was sure to be
near him.

"I'm looking at my bicycle tree," answered
Jody.

Sylvie thought this over. "Does it really
grow bicycles?" she asked.

"In a way it does," said Jody. "Pretty
soon that tree will have some peaches on
it. Then I'll pick those peaches and sell
them. If I can get five dollars for them,
I'll have my bicycle."

Jody was thinking how lucky he was that the bicycle was ready for him now. Fred, his oldest brother, had bought the bicycle six years ago. It had cost more dollars than Jody could count then.

Two years later Fred had grown too large for the bicycle. Then Jack, Jody's second-from-the-top brother, bought it. It had cost Jack ten dollars less than it had cost Fred.

Two years later Jack had grown too large for the bicycle. Jack had to sell it to Tom, the next brother. It cost Tom ten dollars less than it had cost Jack.

Now Tom was ready to sell it to Jody for just ten dollars. This was much less than it had cost Tom.

"I have five dollars right now in my red and white pig bank," said Jody to his sister Sylvie. "I need only five dollars more. I'll pick the peaches off my tree and sell them for five dollars. That is why I call it a bicycle tree."

"When will the peaches come?" asked Sylvie, who was too little to remember when they came last year.

"Pretty soon," said Jody, not really thinking about what his sister had asked.

"May I help pick them?" asked Sylvie.

"Oh, surely," Jody said without thinking.

He tried to count the blossoms on the tree, but there were such a lot of them he couldn't count even those on one branch.

Jody knew that every peach blossom doesn't turn into a peach, but he felt sure that he would have a lot of fine peaches to sell. People would buy them, too. In other years they had bought his peaches. They didn't seem to care how much the peaches cost.

"Pretty!" cried Sylvie, looking at the blossoms on the branches. "May I pick some?"

"Well," said Jody, "I don't know. Every blossom picked may mean one less peach. But there are a lot of blossoms. I guess one small branch won't be missed."

The spring months went by. After the blossoms dropped from the branches, nothing happened for what seemed like a very long time to Jody. He worked at any small jobs that he could get, and in this way earned a little money. With part of the money he bought a can of bright red paint.

"I'll paint the bicycle bright red when I get it," he thought. "It will be the brightest bicycle around here."

Then one day when Jody and Sylvie were looking at the bicycle tree, they found little green peaches where the bright blossoms had been. Jody felt sure that many of these would drop from the branches, but he thought there would be a lot of peaches to pick.

Sylvie pulled down a branch and looked at the little green peaches on it. "Let's pick them now so you can get your bicycle," she said.

"Not yet," said Jody. "They have to be lots larger. We'll have to wait a while."

Sylvie looked a little unhappy. "Next week?" she asked.

"No," said Jody. "Not that soon."

Two weeks passed. Now the peaches looked much bigger to Sylvie. Some of them had dropped off. She gathered a handful out of the grass. "Now we can sell some," she said, smiling brightly.

Jody laughed at his sister. "Not yet," he said. "Those dropped off because they were bad, or because there were more on the branches than the tree could feed."

Sylvie looked unhappy again. Her bright smile was gone.

"Never mind!" said Jody. "Even if we can't sell these peaches or pick any on the tree yet, we can have fun making peach people. It's easy to do. I'll show you how. Watch me.

"I use one peach to make the body and another to make the head. I use little sticks to make arms and legs. See how easy it is?"

Sylvie was soon able to make peach people herself. Jody was happy and surprised to find that she was able to put them together so easily with the sticks he found for her.

While his sister made peach people, Jody stood and looked at his peach tree. It was easier than ever for him to see a bicycle in the tree, now that little peaches were growing on the branches.

A Surprise for Jody

One Saturday morning early in the summer, Tom and Jody were looking at Jody's peaches.

"They look fine!" said Tom. "About five weeks from now they'll be getting ripe."

Just then Sylvie came running out and took hold of Jody's hand. Jody smiled at her and patted her head.

"I'll let them hang on a week longer than that, Tom," he said. "They'll surely be ripe then."

Sylvie didn't wait to hear more. "Just a week!" she thought happily, and off she ran to find sticks for making peach men.

"Well, Tom, it's easy to see that I'll have lots of fine peaches to sell when they are ripe," said Jody. "I'll be able to buy the bicycle, I'm sure."

"How would you like to have a basket to hang on the bicycle?" asked Tom. "If you had a basket you would be able to earn money carrying things for people. I know where you can get one right now."

"How much will the basket cost?" asked Jody. "I won't have much money to spend until my peaches are ripe."

"This basket won't cost much," said Tom. "It's an old one that Mr. White found in his barn. It's not beautiful now, but it will look fine if you paint it bright red to go with your bicycle."

"I'll go over and look at it now," said Jody. "Maybe Mr. White will be able to find work that I can do to earn the basket. Then I won't have to spend any money."

Jody wasn't gone long. He found the basket in pretty good shape. He also found that Mr. White was able to give him a job for the next Saturday. He told Jody that he would give him the basket for helping clean the barn. Jody wouldn't have to spend a cent for it.

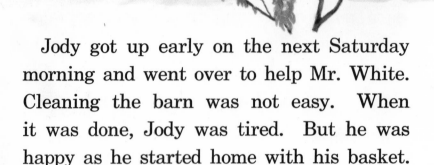

Jody got up early on the next Saturday morning and went over to help Mr. White. Cleaning the barn was not easy. When it was done, Jody was tired. But he was happy as he started home with his basket.

As Jody came near his home, he looked across the garden toward his peach tree. Under the tree he saw his sister. She was dressed in a bright red dress and was very busy.

"Making peach men with sticks and peaches," he thought.

Jody stopped to show the basket to his mother. Then he started toward the tree.

"Look at this, Sylvie!" he called. "I didn't have to spend a cent ——"

And then he stopped, with his mouth wide open and his eyes popping out. There was hardly a peach left hanging on the branches of his beautiful peach tree.

Instead, a large basket was sitting under the tree. It was full of hard green peaches that should not have been picked for five weeks yet.

Sylvie was standing on a box and was using a stick to get a peach that was beyond the reach of her fingers. She looked hot and tired, but she smiled brightly as she turned toward Jody.

"There!" she cried as she dropped the stick and jumped off the box. "I've picked all I can reach. The rest are hanging too high. Now you can get your bicycle right away. Are you surprised?"

"When you are angry, count to ten before you say anything," Jody's father had always told him. "If you don't, you may be sorry."

Jody sat down with his back against the tree. He counted far beyond ten before he was able to answer his sister.

"Yes," he said slowly, "I am surprised." He could hardly get the words out. "But, Sylvie, why did you think that the peaches were ready to pick today?"

"You said so last Saturday," Sylvie answered. "I heard you tell Tom you would wait a week longer. So I waited a week."

Then Jody remembered what had been said, and he knew what had happened.

"Well, Sylvie, perhaps you had better go to the house and rest now," he said.

As Sylvie started toward the house, Jody reached down and picked up a peach. "Why, oh why," he thought, "did I tell her she could help me pick the peaches? Why didn't I tell her they had to be ripe instead of telling her that they had to be a lot bigger?"

For a long time, Jody stayed with his back against the tree. He didn't want anyone to talk about feeling sorry for him. He felt so sad he was afraid he might cry.

"Don't buy anything until you can pay for it." How often Jody had heard his father say that! How could he ever buy that bicycle?

There wasn't a chance to earn money now. The days were so hot that even the grass didn't grow enough to need cutting. Then, too, Jody didn't have a chance to look for jobs. He had to help his father with the farm work every day. It seemed that everything was going against him.

Maybe in the fall — but then a sad thought came to him. Perhaps Tom would find a chance to sell the bicycle before Jody could pay for it.

Jody knew that Tom wanted a watch and that he was saving his money to buy one. Jody also knew that Tom needed only about ten dollars more. If Tom got a chance to sell the bicycle before fall, perhaps he wouldn't want to wait for Jody to earn enough to buy it.

Jody thought, "Well, there isn't much I can do about it now. The more I think about it, the sadder I feel. I'd better work harder and think less. I'll work so hard that I won't have time to feel sad."

During the next few days, Jody worked so hard that Tom began to feel worried.

"Why don't you ever take a rest?" asked Tom. "You're working too hard."

Jody just said, "The busier I am, the less time I have to be sorry about the bicycle. I'll not be able to save enough to buy it this summer."

"Use it any time you want to," said Tom.

"No," said Jody, "that would just make me feel sadder about it."

"Well," said Tom, "I'll take a chance. Pay five dollars down. You can save the rest from what you earn during the fall. Let's ask Dad."

"Thanks just the same, but I guess we had better not," said Jody. "Perhaps Dad would say yes, but he still wouldn't think it was right."

Another Surprise

So Jody kept on working hard during the few long summer days that were left. He was careful to stay away from his peach tree. He didn't want to see it now.

Summer was almost gone. Fall was near, but Jody hardly knew it. He tried to keep from thinking of the fall days when other boys would be riding bicycles to school and he wouldn't be able to have one.

Then the day came for putting up the big red and blue striped sales tent by the road. Jody helped his dad with that work while the other boys picked and carried in baskets of ripe peaches.

The baskets of red and yellow peaches made the sales tent look beautiful. Jody had always liked to sell peaches in the tent. He liked it this year, too, except when he thought that not even one basket of peaches came from his tree.

Jody's dad let him run the stand. Jody could make change, and he knew what to tell people about the different kinds of peaches that were for sale.

"Best salesman I have," said Dad. "Don't know what I'd do without you."

That made Jody feel good. He liked being a salesman. He liked to help people get just what they wanted. He liked to make change, too.

One day a man came who looked over all the baskets of peaches. He didn't seem to find what he wanted.

"My name is Burns," he said. "I want the biggest, nicest peaches that grow. I'm going to send them by plane to my daughter who lives many miles from here. I've sent her oranges and apples before. I think she would like some peaches for a change. I want her to have the finest peaches that grow."

"These Big Goldens are nice," said Jody.

"They are nice in every way except size. They are not big enough," said Mr. Burns.

"How about these Red Princess peaches?" asked Jody, reaching down to pick up some very nice-looking ones.

Mr. Burns was not pleased yet. "Still not big enough," he said. "I want to make my daughter's eyes pop out."

"Well," said Jody, "I'm afraid ——"

"Perhaps he would like to look at the peaches on your tree," said Jody's father, who had set down a basket of peaches and stopped to listen.

Jody tried to smile. "There are no peaches on my tree, Mr. Burns," he said sadly. "Dad is joking."

"No, Jody," said his father. "I'm not joking. There are just a few, but they are certainly the nicest, biggest peaches I've ever seen."

"Let me see them!" said Mr. Burns. "Perhaps they'll do for a present for my daughter."

"Come with me," said Jody, as he started toward the garden. He couldn't believe that they would find any peaches. Perhaps his dad had looked at the wrong tree.

As they walked toward the tree, Jody's eyes took in every branch. On the topmost branch there certainly was something, and it certainly was yellow.

Jody was so excited he couldn't wait for Mr. Burns. He ran ahead to the tree and climbed into it.

"Oh, my!" said Jody, his mouth wide open in surprise as he looked up.

There, far beyond the reach of Sylvie's fingers or her stick, were some of the biggest peaches Jody had ever seen. He picked one and showed it to Mr. Burns.

"They are as big as footballs," said Mr. Burns, putting his head up through the branches. "I'm certainly lucky. What a present those will make for my daughter!"

They were not really as big as footballs, but they were certainly bigger than any peaches Jody had ever seen. The colors of red and yellow were beautiful, too.

Jody couldn't think how they could have grown so big until he remembered what his father had said once.

"If a tree has just a few peaches on it," his father had said, "those few get an extra lot of food. Extra food makes peaches that are extra big and extra nice."

"How many of these have you?" asked Mr. Burns. "I'll take every one of them!"

"I don't know for certain," said Jody, looking over the top branches. "It will take only a few peaches of this size to fill a basket. I think there will be nearly a basketful."

"Good," said Mr. Burns. "Those are extra large and extra nice peaches. I'll pay you a little extra for them. What would you say to five dollars for the lot?"

"Fine!" said Jody. "I'll pick them right now and hand them to you."

Mr. Burns took each peach and put it carefully into a basket.

"These peaches will certainly surprise and please my daughter," he said.

"Not nearly so much as they surprised and pleased me," thought Jody happily.

Watch Those Meanings!

Many words that you know have more than one meaning. To find out what meaning a word has in a sentence, you must use the meaning of the other words that are used with it.

The word **dress** has two widely different meanings. When you **dress** as an Indian chief, you put on Indian clothes and wear a headdress made of feathers.

Before a chicken is cooked, it is **dressed.** Does this mean that someone puts clothes and a feather headdress on it? No, all the chicken's feathers are pulled out.

What two meanings does the word **pass** have in these two sentences?

Please **pass** the butter to me, Dot.

We'll **pass** Tom's house on the way home.

Think of different meanings of the word **band.** Use these questions to help you.

What kind of **band** plays music?

What kind of **band** stretches easily?

What kind of **band** is put on a hat?

What is a **band** of men?

In the following sentences the words printed in very black letters may be new to you. You can read them by using good sense and beginning sounds to help you.

When you come to a new word, read the rest of the sentence. Then think what the new word should be to make sense there. Next answer this question: Does the word you thought of begin with the same sound as the new word? If it doesn't, try again.

A bird can't change clothes the way you can. It has only one **coat** to wear, a feather coat. That one coat is its work coat, dress coat, overcoat, and **raincoat.**

In cold winter **weather,** the bird's feather coat helps keep it **warm.**

In **wet,** rainy weather, the same feather coat helps keep the bird **dry.**

Do birds ever wash their clothes? Of **course** they do. When they **splash** around in water, they are washing their coats and taking a **bath** at the same time.

One Word Instead of Two

In books you will often find words that have the ending **n't.** If such a word seems strange, look at it carefully. It is almost sure to be a word that you use often in talking. It is the kind of word that does the work of two words.

When we say **didn't,** we mean **did not.** We use the ending **n't** instead of **not.** When we write or print a word that ends in **n't,** we put in the mark ' to show that the letter **o** has been left out.

Write each of the following words and the two words it stands for.

wasn't	**haven't**	**doesn't**	**couldn't**
wouldn't	**weren't**	**hadn't**	**mustn't**
shouldn't	**oughtn't**	**aren't**	**needn't**

When your pet has done something he oughtn't or shouldn't, it doesn't help much to shout at him, "Don't!"

That doesn't undo what has happened. It couldn't. Just teach him how not to do wrong. Then he won't.

Sometimes the mark ' stands for two or more letters that have been left out. When we write or print **I've** instead of **I have,** the mark stands for the two letters **ha**. The ending **'ve** always means **have**.

The ending **'d** in such words as **I'd, he'd,** or **you'd** means **would, should,** or **had**. The mark stands for **woul, shoul,** or **ha**.

The ending **'ll** in **I'll, they'll,** and **we'll** means **will** or **shall**. The mark stands for **wi** or **sha**.

Think what two words each word in very black letters stands for in these sentences:

"Bill, **you'd** better put down that book or **we'll** miss the show!" Bob called.

"Dad said **he'd** take us," said Bill. "He **hasn't** come back yet, has he?"

"Not yet," said Bob, "but he told Mother and Ann **they'd** better be ready before seven. **They've** just gone downstairs. Dad **doesn't** like to wait, you know."

"**I'll** not take any chances," said Bill. "**He'd** go without us and then laugh at us, **wouldn't** he? **I'll** put the book away."

There are other short words that are used instead of two words.

The ending **'re** means **are.** You see it in the word **we're.** **We're** means **we are.**

The ending **'m** is used with the word **I** to make **I'm.** **I'm** means **I am.**

The ending **'s** may mean **is** or **has.** The word **she's** may mean **she is** or **she has.** **That's** may mean **that is** or **that has.**

Think what two words each of the very black words in these sentences stands for:

Where's Betty? **She's** never been late before. **Dad's** been looking for her and Dot. **They're** playing along the way, I guess. **I'm** sure **that's** happened before. **It's** nothing new or strange.

The ending **'s** doesn't always mean **is** or **has.** Sometimes it means about the same as **belonging to.**

Think what the ending **'s** means in each place it is used in these sentences:

I hope **Dad's** car is ready. **He's** had plenty of time to call us on the telephone. **I'll** be glad when **he's** back home.

Presents for Mother

"We've done a pretty good job, if you ask me," said Dick Greenwood to his sister Agnes and his small brother Andy. "Now if you two will carry this trunk and that box upstairs to the storeroom, my room will be in tiptop shape."

"You just hop down and do some carrying yourself," said Agnes. "Andy is too little to help carry boxes and trunks around."

"I don't want the box moved anyway," said Andy, climbing into the box as he talked. "It's more fun to have it right here. Let's play Jack-in-the-box."

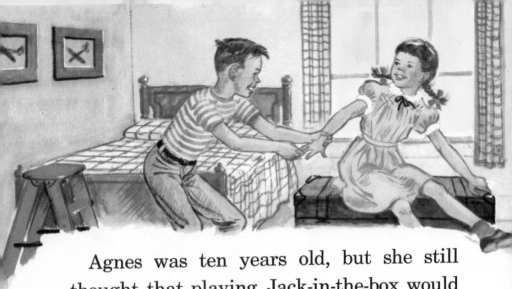

Agnes was ten years old, but she still thought that playing Jack-in-the-box would be fun. Since, however, she was the only girl in the family, she knew that she should help her mother.

"Well, we'll have to get them out of here soon," she said. "You know that Mother wants the house to be neat and tidy before Thanksgiving."

"It's days and days until Thanksgiving," Andy said happily as he got down in the box and covered his head.

"It's not such a very long time," said Dick. "We have a lot of things to do. Mother's birthday comes on Thanksgiving this year. Has anybody thought about what to give her?"

"I've been thinking about it for weeks," said Agnes. "Last year I gave her some beautiful earrings. I thought she might start wearing them, but she didn't. She gave them away. Mother's such a problem!"

"Yes, she is," said Dick. "I wish we could think of something she would really want to keep. Then each of us could put in some of his spending money and help buy it for her."

"She'd keep a present, I think, if she remembered that we gave it to her," said Agnes. "But after a few months she forgets who gave her what.

"Once I saw her looking at some presents we had bought for her. 'Where in the world did this truck come from?' she asked. How could I tell her when she called them truck?"

"What happened to them?" asked Dick.

"That time our presents went to the Children's Home," said Agnes. "That was all right, because I don't think Mother really liked those presents.

"I think the real trouble is that we have always bought her something we liked ourselves. When she and Daddy get us a present, they think about what we like and what we want.

"When we get something from them, we're pleased. Do you think we have ever given Mother anything that excited her as much as my bicycle excited me last year?"

No one answered.

"Well, I don't," Agnes said, "and I'm sure that if we get her something that she really wants, she'll keep it."

Dick jumped up in the air and landed on the bed. "That's easy!" he cried. "We just have to ask her what she wants."

"That won't work," said his sister. "I tried it. She said that this old farmhouse was the best present she could have. She has always wanted to live on a farm."

"But it's not a surprise," said Dick, "and it belongs to all of us, really. Besides, we didn't give it to her."

The Jack-in-the-box popped his head out of the box. "I know what she wants," he said. The Jack-in-the-box went down again.

In a second Dick and Agnes were beside the box, looking down at Andy.

"How do you know what she wants?" asked Agnes.

Andy's round little face looked up at her. "You should know. She's told you often enough."

"When? What did she tell us?" Dick wanted to know.

"Even when we lived in the city Mother kept saying she wanted to keep chickens," said Andy. "And now ——"

"That's right!" broke in Dick.

"And since we've been here I've heard her say plenty of times that she wanted some chickens," said Agnes.

Dick laughed. "That makes it easy," he said. "At a farm up the road there's a sign that says EGGS FOR SALE. Let's go right away and see if they'll sell us three chickens. Each of us will give one to Mother. Come on!"

"Do we have enough money?" asked Agnes.

"If we don't, I know what we can do," answered Dick. "Let's go."

Andy popped out of the box and began putting on his snowsuit and overshoes. He was almost six and well able to dress himself, except when he was in a hurry and tried to put on everything at once.

This time, Dick and Agnes each took a leg to hurry things up.

Chickens for Sale

In a surprisingly short time they were knocking at the door of the farmhouse.

It was opened by a woman with gray hair which should have stayed high on her head, but it didn't. A few pieces were hanging down beside her kindly, round face. "Hello," she said. "Come right in."

She smiled at Andy and said, "You're the new city people from down the road, I guess."

"Yes," answered Dick. Because he was the oldest of the three, he felt that he should do the talking. "We came to ask about chickens. Do you have any for sale?"

"We certainly do, if you don't want them in too much of a hurry," said the woman.

"We don't want them until the night before Thanksgiving," said Dick. "We'd like three."

"You want them dressed, don't you?" the woman asked.

Andy laughed. "Dressed!" he cried. "You don't dress them up, do you?"

The farmer's wife laughed too. "Not in suits and dresses," she said. "I pull out the feathers. Then I clean the chickens for cooking."

"Oh, NO!" the children cried together.

"We want live chickens," said Dick. "They're to be a birthday present for Mother. We all hope they'll be something she really wants."

"Does she want chickens more than anything else?" asked the woman.

"We think she does," Agnes said, "and we do want to give her a present she can't throw away and won't give away."

The woman wanted to hear all about it. She asked a number of questions. When she told Dick how much the chickens would cost, he counted out the change the three of them had.

"We don't have enough here," he said. "But we can pay the rest of it if you will let us pay by the week. Could you please let us do that?"

The farmer's wife laughed. "I never have done that," she answered, "but I might if you'll give me your promise to pay."

"Daddy gives us spending money every week for ourselves," said Dick. "We'll save that and pay you with it. Do you have a pencil and paper that I could use?"

Dick sat down at the kitchen table and thought hard. Soon he began to put some words down on the paper. Agnes and Andy wanted to watch, but he waved them away.

"Now," he said at last, "listen to this":

> We promise to pay 50¢ every Monday. If something happens so we can't pay, we promise to work on Saturdays doing any farm jobs you want until we earn all the money.
>
> Dick Greenwood

"That's all I need," said the farmer's wife. "I'll certainly believe anyone who is able to make up a paper like that."

Nothing exciting happened until the day before Thanksgiving. Then the children faced a real problem. At first it seemed as if there would never be a time when they would be able to get the chickens home without being seen or heard.

After all, it isn't easy to hide full-grown chickens. They get excited easily and let out loud squawks that can be heard near and far.

It was lucky for the children that Mother remembered some groceries she had to buy in town. But it was late when she and Daddy drove off in the car.

"Come on," Dick said. "We've got to hurry. There is less time than I thought we'd have. We have to get those chickens home and get them to sleep before Mother comes back."

Happy Birthday!

The chickens were ready for them in the farm kitchen — one white hen, one brown hen, and a fine large rooster with black feathers. The farmer's wife put the rooster in Dick's arms, the brown hen in Andy's arms, and the white hen in Agnes's arms.

"Hold on to their legs," she said.

The three children started toward home.

On the way Dick thought of something. "Let's name the chickens for ourselves," he said. "Then Mother can never forget that we gave them to her."

Agnes was pleased with this and began to talk to the hen she was carrying. "Hello, Agnes, how are you?" she said.

84

But Andy stopped in the middle of the road. "I want to go back and get another chicken," he said.

"Why?" asked the others.

"Because mine's a hen. You can't call a hen Andy. That's a boy's name."

They all stopped to think over that problem.

"Chickens don't really care what their names are," said Dick. "You can call them whatever you like."

"All right, then, give me yours," said Andy. "We'll call the brown hen Dick."

"Don't be silly. I'm the oldest, so I get the biggest chicken," said Dick. "Besides, I've already named him Dick."

For just a second Andy was angry. In that second he let go of the brown hen's legs. The hen scooted out of his arms.

"Catch her! Catch her!" shouted Dick and Agnes. "Don't let her get away."

They were not able to help Andy catch the hen, because they were holding their own chickens, but they shouted everything they could think of for him to do.

The brown hen ran every which way, squawking loudly and making her wings go up and down. Every time Andy got near enough to try to take hold of her tail feathers, she gave a loud squawk, jumped into the air, and ran off beyond his reach.

Andy was getting too tired to make a sound. It was getting dark, and there was not much time. Just then the headlights of a car showed far away down the road.

"Look out!" cried Agnes. "Hide! Perhaps it's Mother and Daddy." She jumped behind the small trees beside the road, and Dick followed her.

Andy stopped for a second. The car was still a long way off and coming slowly. There was plenty of time. He looked at the brown hen. She looked as tired as he felt. Anyhow, she was walking along slowly right by him.

Andy reached down and picked her up. It was as easy as that. Then he went to hide behind the trees as the car went by.

"It wasn't Daddy," Agnes said, "but we had better hurry home anyway."

No one said anything again until all six, three children and three chickens, were in the storeroom. They were hiding the chickens there because the room was upstairs where a few squawks and other strange noises might not be heard.

"I'm glad that's over!" said Agnes, setting her hen down on a box.

"What shall we do now?" asked Andy.

"We must go out one at a time and not make any noise," whispered Dick. "We'll leave the chickens in the dark. Then they'll be quiet."

"And what will we do in the morning?" asked Agnes.

"I know how we'll give them to Mother," said Dick. "We'll get up while it's still dark and come up here very quietly and get the chickens. Then we'll go down to Mother's bedroom.

"Andy will run in, holding his chicken, and turn on the light. Then we'll come in with our chickens and shout 'Happy Birthday!' "

"That's a good way to do it," said Agnes. "But we haven't finished naming the chickens. Let's call the brown hen Ann. That's almost like Andy. Lots of girls are named for their fathers that way. I'm sure a hen named Ann would always make Mother think of Andy."

Andy thought that would be all right. "I don't mind," he said. "That mean old hen picked at me with her bill when I was carrying her home."

Then Agnes thought of something. "Let's hang a card with a name on it around each chicken's neck. Then Mother won't be able to forget their names."

"I'm glad you thought of that," said Dick. "I'll make the cards right now."

Very early Thanksgiving morning, while it was still dark outside, Mrs. Greenwood woke up. At first she kept her eyes shut, thinking how good it was to live on a farm.

Suddenly she sat upright in bed.

"Bob!" she cried. "I hear something in the storeroom."

"Don't be silly!" Mr. Greenwood said.

"Listen!" said Mrs. Greenwood.

They both listened. Yes, something was certainly making strange little noises in the storeroom.

"I wish you would go to see what's making that noise," said Mrs. Greenwood.

Mr. Greenwood waited and listened.

"I don't hear it any more," he said. He turned over and tried to go back to sleep.

"Bob," Mrs. Greenwood called again. "I heard the noise again. Only this time it sounded right outside our door. Please get up and see what it is."

"Oh, all right," said Mr. Greenwood. "Wait until I find the light."

Suddenly the door opened. "Happy birth-!" the children began. But that was as far as they got.

Andy was in such a hurry to turn on the light that he fell over a chair. "Oh, dear," his mother heard him say. "I've dropped Ann, and now I can't find the light."

Dick ran to help Andy. Andy's hen flew right into Dick and frightened both Dick and the rooster he was carrying. The rooster gave a squawk and jumped out of Dick's arms. Agnes came running in. She was so excited that she dropped her hen.

The two chickens and the rooster went this way and that in the dark, flying, running, and squawking loudly.

"Help! Help! Take them away!" cried Mrs. Greenwood as she pulled the bedclothes over her head.

Mr. Greenwood jumped out of bed and turned on the light. By this time the chickens had landed on the bed and had quieted down. The children stood still, their eyes popping, as Mrs. Greenwood came out from under the bedclothes.

"Chickens!" cried Mrs. Greenwood.

The children were not sure she was pleased.

"You said you wanted to keep chickens," said Andy. "Aren't they pretty?"

Mrs. Greenwood was too surprised to answer.

"See the cards hanging around their necks?" said Dick. "We named the chickens for ourselves so that you'd have something to remember us by."

"The brown hen is named for me," said Andy, "but we had to call him Ann instead of Andy, because he is a girl."

Mrs. Greenwood smiled at Andy, but she still seemed unable to talk.

"You are pleased, aren't you, Mother?" asked Agnes. "You know how much you wanted chickens. You won't give them away, will you?"

Mrs. Greenwood smiled happily at her daughter. "I certainly will not," she promised. "You three couldn't have picked a present that I wanted more.

"And I will always remember their names — Dick, Agnes, and Ann."

Merry-Go-Round

I climbed up on the merry-go-round,
And it went round and round.

I climbed up on a big brown horse,
And it went up and down.

Around and round
And up and down,
Around and round
And up and down.
I sat high up
On a big brown horse
And rode around
On the merry-go-round
And rode around.

On the merry-go-round
I rode around
On the merry-go-round
Around
And round
And round.

When I Go Fishing

When I go fishing,
I'm always wishing
Some fishes I will get;
But while I'm fishing,
The fish are wishing
I won't — just harder yet.

And of those wishes
Of the fishes
Every one comes true;
So all my wishes
To get fishes
Never, never do.

Can Printed Words Talk?

Do you know that the printed sentences in books are just printed talk? When you read a story silently, do you think how the sentences would sound if someone were telling the story to you?

When someone thinks up a good story, he wants to tell it. He feels sure that most people would like to hear it. But he knows that only a few can ever get near enough to hear him talk. So what does he do?

He writes the story on paper. If it is a good story, it may be printed in a book for you to read. When you open the book, you see the story that the writer wants you to hear. There is his printed talk. Can you hear it? You can try.

Here is one way to do it. Read the story silently. As you read each sentence, think how it would sound if you heard a storyteller saying it. By doing that, you can make it seem that you are really hearing the story the printed words tell.

At the Fair

Everyone likes to go to a fair, because there is so much to see and do there.

Our big fairs take place on large fair grounds. In the big buildings there are places for people to put the things they want to show. Outside the buildings there is room for tents, games, races, and food stands.

Men and women and boys and girls from far and near bring their best cows, pigs, sheep, or other animals to show at the fair. Each one hopes that the judges will say that his animals are the best of their kind.

Anyone can bring an animal to the fair to be judged. The animals that are judged to be best win blue ribbons. Sometimes an animal wins both money and a blue ribbon.

Prizes and blue ribbons are given for almost everything that can be grown on a farm. The fresh fruits and vegetables that are shown at a fair are so large and beautiful that they hardly seem real.

Prizes are given also for canned goods. In that part of the fair there will be shelf after shelf of glass jars filled with the finest fruits and vegetables that grow. The colors are something to remember always.

The women and girls bring their best cakes, cookies, and pies to the fair. Women who win prizes for pies, cakes, or something else they have baked are known for miles around as fine cooks.

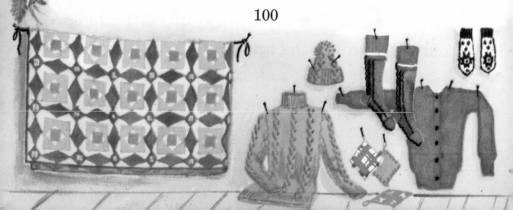

Besides canning fruit and vegetables and baking pies and cakes, the women and girls make a lot of handwork for the fair. They bring dresses, hats, tablecloths, baby clothes, and many other beautiful things that they have made.

Everyone at a fair has a good time looking at everything, but there are lots of things to do, too. There are merry-go-rounds and other rides even more exciting. There are shows that are almost as good as circuses. There are places to buy all kinds of good things to eat.

If you look carefully at the pictures of a fair shown here, you will find many things that you might see at a fair. If you have been to a fair, perhaps you can tell the boys and girls in school about it.

Jeremiah woke up and heard the icy wind whistling through his partly open window.

"Even if spring is nearly here," he thought, "winter hasn't left yet."

It felt good to be in bed on such a night. Jeremiah pulled the bedcovers up high around his neck to keep out the cold.

Then he heard a cry. At once he knew what it was. The new lamb had come.

The thought of leaving his warm bed was almost too much for Jeremiah. But he knew that he should get up and go to the barn. Someone had to make certain that the new lamb and its mother were warm enough.

Granny heard Jeremiah getting dressed.

"Jeremiah," she called, "what are you doing up at this time of night?"

"I think the new lamb has come, Granny," answered Jeremiah. "I'm going out to the barn to make sure everything is all right."

"I'll come too," said Granny. "You'll probably need me. Just listen to that wind! It sounds as if it could blow our whole barn away. Put on your warmest clothes. The barn won't be warm."

By the time Granny was ready, Jeremiah was waiting at the back door with a light.

Facing into the wind, they hurried to the barn. It was all they could do to open the big door against the wind. Then suddenly they were safely inside the barn, which really felt warm to them now.

"Look!" said Jeremiah, as he ran over
to the sheep pen in one corner of the barn.
"It's happened! Isn't that the nicest little
white lamb you ever saw?"

Granny bent over the side of the pen to
look. "It surely is," she said. "The mother
seems to think so too. See how close to her
new daughter she stays. She is keeping
her warm and safe."

And then they saw him. He was away
over in one corner of the pen, cold,
frightened, and alone. Unlike his twin,
he was as black as night. Jeremiah
thought he had never seen anything so
beautiful as that little black lamb.

"She probably won't take care of him,"
said Granny, who knew all about sheep.

"Let's see if she'll feed him," Jeremiah
said, as he bent down to pick up the lamb.

But it was just as Granny had said. The
mother sheep would not let her new son
stay close to her. Instead, she put her
head down and pushed the poor little black
lamb part way across the pen.

The lamb dropped down on the floor of
the pen and cried softly. He was cold,
frightened, and hungry.

"No use, son," said Granny. "She refuses
to have him, and that's all there is to it.
Don't try to make her take him."

"But he won't live if she refuses to take
care of him," said Jeremiah, trying hard
to keep back the tears.

"We don't want a black sheep anyhow," said Granny. "Everyone knows how much trouble a black sheep can make."

Jeremiah bent down and put his arms around the little lamb. The lamb pushed his soft nose against Jeremiah's neck. Jeremiah held him close.

'I want him more than anything else in the world," he said.

"He'll be nothing but trouble," said Granny. "How will you feed him?"

"I'll teach him to take milk from a dish," said Jeremiah. "He's a smart lamb. He'll learn fast."

"Where will you put him?" she asked.

"In a basket in our kitchen," Jeremiah said. "He'll be safe and warm there, and he won't get into trouble. Please let me keep him, Granny."

When Granny saw how much Jeremiah wanted the soft black lamb, she couldn't refuse to let the boy keep him.

"All right," she said, "but you must take care of him all by yourself."

"You won't be sorry, Granny," said Jeremiah. "I'll see that he is no trouble to you at all. I'm going to teach him to do tricks. You'll see how smart he will be. I've even thought up a name for him."

"What is it?" asked Granny.

"Midnight," said Jeremiah. "That's because he's as black as midnight, and it was midnight when we first saw him."

Granny found a bag that chicken feed had come in. "Here," she said, "put this around him to keep him warm. Then bring him into the house. I'll fix some warm milk for him."

"Midnight," said Jeremiah softly, as he held the bag closely around the lamb. "Midnight, you and I are going to be great friends."

Things turned out just as Granny had said they would. In a few days Midnight learned how to tip over his basket and get out. From then on he was into everything in the house.

By the time the first warm days came, Midnight was able to go outdoors. After that he kept close to Jeremiah wherever he went. Midnight was like Jeremiah's shadow, always close behind him.

Midnight liked to butt his head against things. One day he butted the clothes basket and tipped out all Granny's clean clothes. Jeremiah may have thought that was a smart trick. Granny did not.

Then one day Midnight butted poor Granny hard and almost knocked her down. He probably thought that was great fun, but she didn't.

"Jeremiah," she said, "if your wonderful Midnight tips over my nice white wash again or butts me once more, I'll fix him. I'll cook him until he's a beautiful brown, and I'll eat him for my dinner!"

Midnight Gets into Trouble

One Saturday Jeremiah, with a penny in his pocket, went down the road to Banks Corner and Mr. Grundy's store. Midnight followed close behind him like a little black shadow. Every once in a while he butted Jeremiah playfully.

Banks Corner was about a mile from the farm. It was a very small place, but to Jeremiah, Banks Corner was wonderful.

It was most wonderful when a train came whistling through. Jeremiah had never been on a train. He often wished that he could ride on one.

When Jeremiah got to Banks Corner, he went right into Mr. Grundy's store, walked over to the candy counter, and pushed his nose against the glass.

His black shadow came right behind him just as if he too had a penny to spend.

"Get that black lamb out of here," said Mr. Grundy. "I've heard all about him. I don't want him butting things around in my store."

"I want to buy some candy," Jeremiah said. "I'll keep Midnight right beside me."

"Well, buy your candy fast and get that trouble-maker out of here," said Mr. Grundy. He smiled as he said it, so Jeremiah knew he really wasn't angry.

Midnight was so quiet that Jeremiah kept on looking. It was hard to decide what to choose. All the candy looked wonderful.

Then it happened. A train whistled for the crossing. It frightened Midnight, and he began to run wildly around the store.

110

He butted into the pans and pails that were hanging up on one side of the store. Down they came. This frightened Midnight more than ever. He knocked jars and boxes off the candy counter. The floor was covered with candy and broken glass.

He leaped wildly over the grocery counter and knocked groceries all over the floor.

Mr. Grundy decided that something had to be done. He picked up a broom and tried to chase Midnight out of the store.

Two of the men who were in the back of the store were greatly excited.

"Go it, lamb!" shouted one of them.

"Go it, Grundy!" shouted the other.

Just then Jeremiah's Uncle Hiram came into the store. He saw at once what was happening. As the frightened lamb tried to leap over the candy counter, Uncle Hiram caught him. The wild chase was over.

Midnight was surprised at being caught. He hadn't seen Uncle Hiram at all.

Jeremiah took Midnight in his arms. "I'm sorry for what happened, Mr. Grundy," he said. "I'll pay for it. Here's my penny. It will help some. It's all I have now."

"Forget it, son," said Mr. Grundy. "You can always be sure that a black sheep will get into trouble. Just plan to keep him out of my store after this. Now go ahead and pick out the candy you want."

"Thank you, Mr. Grundy," said Jeremiah, "but I'll pay you when I get some money."

Jeremiah knew that he had to plan some way to earn the money. Perhaps Uncle Hiram would help him plan what to do.

The next Saturday Jeremiah was teaching Midnight to jump over a stick.

"You're the handsomest lamb in the whole world," said Jeremiah. "You're the smartest, too. You'd take a prize at any fair."

Suddenly Jeremiah began to dance around.

"At any fair!" he shouted. "That's it, Midnight! I'll take you to the state fair. You'll win the blue ribbon and the cash prize too. Then I can pay Mr. Grundy. You'll earn the money yourself."

Midnight leaped around as if he wanted to say, "One blue ribbon? Why, I'll win two blue ribbons if you want me to."

Jeremiah ran to tell his plan to Granny.

"No!" said Granny. "No, indeed! That good-for-nothing black sheep couldn't win any prize. I've never heard of a black sheep that won anything."

"But, Granny," said Jeremiah, "I'm sure Midnight would get a prize. If he won a cash prize, maybe I would have enough money to pay for what he did to Mr. Grundy's store. He's really the best and most beautiful lamb in the world."

"We are not going to any fair with that lamb," said Granny. "And that's all there is to it. Don't think any more about it."

"But everybody goes to the state fair, Granny," answered Jeremiah. "And what if Midnight really did win the blue ribbon and the cash prize?"

"What if pigs could fly!" said Granny.

A little later Jeremiah was out behind the house telling his plan to Uncle Hiram.

"Midnight's a fine little black lamb," said Jeremiah proudly. "If he won a cash prize, I could pay Mr. Grundy."

"He's a good enough lamb, indeed," said Uncle Hiram. "It's too bad that he's black. The judges may refuse to give a prize to a black lamb. But it won't hurt anything to try. What does Granny say?"

"She won't let me try," said Jeremiah.

Uncle Hiram smiled at Jeremiah. "Sometimes Granny changes her mind," he said. "I think we can fix things. Leave that job to me."

Jeremiah jumped up and down. "Oh, Uncle Hiram!" he cried. His eyes were shining.

That night Uncle Hiram picked up one of Granny's glasses of grape jelly and held it up to let the light shine through it.

"Look, Jeremiah!" he said. "Isn't that the most beautiful grape jelly you ever saw? Such color! Just look at it shine! And it is as sweet as sweet can be. There's no one else in the state who can make grape jelly as good as Granny's."

"If I do say so myself, and I shouldn't," said Granny proudly, "I do make pretty good jelly."

"Pretty good, indeed!" said Uncle Hiram. "It's the best! It would win a first prize at any fair. Now that's a thought. Why not take your grape jelly to the state fair this summer? It will be a sure winner."

116

Granny held the jelly up to the light. "It is pretty," she said. "And people do seem to like it. Our grapes make the sweetest jelly anywhere around. Perhaps I should try for a prize with it."

"Granny, may I take Midnight too?" asked Jeremiah eagerly.

"Why, it will probably be safe to take him along," said Granny, as she got up from the table. "But you mustn't feel sad if he doesn't win a prize. I know he can't win."

Uncle Hiram bent over and whispered in Jeremiah's ear, "I told you I would fix things with Granny. I knew that sweet grape jelly would do the trick."

All Aboard!

All that summer Jeremiah thought about the state fair. He waited eagerly for that special day when Granny and he would take the train to State City and the fair.

One day late in the summer, Uncle Hiram came over with his clippers. He said to Jeremiah, "It will soon be time for the fair. We must get Midnight ready for it."

"What shall we do?" asked Jeremiah.

"Well, first," said Uncle Hiram, "we want to make that soft black wool shine. We'll wash him. Your special job is to hold him while I do the washing. He leaps around so much that I don't think I can hold him and wash him too."

After Midnight's wool was washed so that it was shining in the sun, Uncle Hiram picked up his clippers.

"Why the clippers, Uncle Hiram?" asked Jeremiah.

"You just hold Midnight tight and leave that to me," said Uncle Hiram.

"The judges won't like a lamb with his wool clipped off," said Jeremiah.

"I'm not going to clip him the way you think," said Uncle Hiram. "Watch me."

"Why, you're making him as square as a box," said Jeremiah.

"All prize sheep are clipped this special way to make their backs look wide," said Uncle Hiram. "The best wool on a sheep grows on his back. The wider his back is, the more good wool he has.

"We'll make Midnight look like a real prize sheep. We want to be proud of him even if he can't win any prize."

When Uncle Hiram had finished clipping Midnight, even Granny was surprised.

"Why, he's really beautiful with that square clipping!" she said. "Now, Jeremiah, all you have to do is to keep him from butting the judges out of the fair."

That night, after Uncle Hiram had gone, Jeremiah held Midnight tight and said, "We'll show them, Midnight. You'll be the most beautiful lamb there. You'll win the blue ribbon and a cash prize too."

At last the morning of the great day arrived. Jeremiah and Granny put on their very best clothes. Granny had her jelly in a neat bundle. They arrived at the railroad station long before the train came.

Midnight was shut up tight in a special box that Uncle Hiram had fixed for him. His square clipped wool was shining. Already he was acting as if going to a fair was something he did every day.

Even when the train arrived, Midnight didn't act frightened.

Jeremiah felt certain that nothing could be more wonderful than riding on that shiny train. He wished that all his friends at home could see him now. At times, though, he was a little worried about Midnight.

"Do you think Midnight will act all right when we get to the fair, Granny?" he asked.

"If he does, it will be the first time," said Granny. "But," she went on, "he acted all right getting on the train. Perhaps we can keep him out of trouble.

"I'm glad that I can keep my bundle here where I can take care of it. Jelly jars get broken easily."

The train whistled four times at every crossing. It was a wonderful whistle, and Jeremiah liked to hear it, but he hoped that it was not frightening Midnight. He was sure, though, that Midnight couldn't get out of his special box.

At first when Jeremiah had looked out the train window, the houses were far apart. Then as the train had come nearer to the city they were closer together.

Now the houses were crowded together. Jeremiah thought that this was probably State City. Sure enough, the train began to slow down and soon stopped. A sign on the station said: STATE CITY.

Jeremiah took Granny's bundle and stepped down onto the station platform. He looked around eagerly. Far down the platform he saw a box being taken off one of the cars. He hurried down there.

Midnight acted as though he hadn't minded the train ride at all. He looked out at Jeremiah as if he wanted to say, "Well, here we are! What comes next?"

The Judges Decide

There was a car at the station to take people to the fair. The driver smiled when he saw Midnight and Granny's bundle.

"You may be a little crowded," he said, "but it's not far to the fair grounds."

He took them to a large square building in the fair grounds. People there told them just what to do. Granny found the place for her jelly, and Jeremiah took Midnight to the pens for the lambs.

As Jeremiah was taking Midnight out of his special box, a man said, "That's a fine lamb. Too bad he's black. The judges won't give a black lamb a prize even though they may like him."

"Well," said Jeremiah, "they've never seen a black lamb like Midnight."

When Jeremiah saw how many lambs there were in the pens, he was a little frightened. They were all snow white and all beautiful. Midnight was the only black lamb at the fair.

"The judges will see him, anyway," said Granny. "He's different from any of the others. Now let's go out and see the fair."

Jeremiah had expected the fair to be big, but he had not expected so much noise, so many people, and so many different things.

One building was filled with horses, cows, pigs, and sheep. Another was filled with wonderful fruits and vegetables.

There was a merry-go-round playing loud music all the time. There were all kinds of things to eat. But Granny and Jeremiah didn't take much time to look around. She had to get back to her grape jelly, and he had to get back to Midnight.

In the pen with Midnight was a beautiful white lamb. His wool was the whitest Jeremiah had ever seen. Jeremiah decided that, except for Midnight, that white lamb was the most beautiful lamb there.

Now three men were ready to judge the spring lambs. A large crowd gathered around the pens.

The judges stopped at every pen and looked at each lamb carefully. Sometimes they stepped right into a pen to feel the legs, head, and back of a lamb. One judge kept writing something on a piece of paper.

After a long time the three judges arrived at Midnight's pen. They looked at the two lambs there.

"Well, well! I didn't expect to see a black one," said one of the judges. He laughed as he said it.

125

Though Jeremiah didn't like the way the judge laughed, he did nothing to show it.

Then that judge stepped into the pen and bent over to touch the white lamb. Midnight didn't like that, and he did something to show it. He put his head down and butted the judge as hard as he could.

Down went the judge. He hadn't expected to be butted. He looked very red and very angry as he got up. He became redder when he heard the people laughing at him. The judges walked away.

Jeremiah's eyes filled with tears.

"Oh, Midnight, why did you have to do that?" he thought. "Now you'll never win the prize."

After a while the judges came back. They stopped not far off and talked softly together. Jeremiah could see that they were almost ready to pick the winning lamb.

They kept turning to look at Midnight. The two judges looked at what the third judge had been writing. At last they seemed to agree about something. They all walked over to the corner of the pen where Midnight stood. Each of them looked at him carefully.

Then they looked again at the beautiful white lamb. Once more they stood and talked quietly.

At last the judge who had been butted by Midnight came toward Jeremiah. "Tell me about your lamb, son," he said kindly.

As Jeremiah told the story of Midnight, all the judges gathered around him. They listened very carefully.

"Jeremiah," said the judge who had been writing on the paper, "your lamb is a new kind to us. At first we weren't sure just how we could judge him, but we didn't let that stop us.

"We agreed on two things about your lamb. He's black, and he likes to butt. We also agreed that his butting doesn't keep him from being a fine animal.

"I am pleased to tell you, Jeremiah, that your lamb, Midnight, has won both the blue ribbon for the best spring lamb and the special cash prize for the best lamb in the whole fair."

On the way home, Jeremiah and Granny agreed that it had been a wonderful fair.

Suddenly Jeremiah thought of something.

"Granny," he asked, "did the judges look at your grape jelly? I forgot about it!"

Granny smiled proudly. "They did," she said. "Your black trouble-maker isn't the only one who won a first prize. We won two blue ribbons and two cash prizes."

Just then the train began to slow down.

"Granny! Granny!" shouted Jeremiah. "This is Banks Corner! We're home!"

"What's all that noise?" asked Granny.

"That's for us," said Jeremiah proudly. "People here have probably heard the news already. There's a crowd waiting at the station. Isn't it good to be home!"

"It is, indeed," agreed Granny. "And to be two prize-winners!"

When we talk about the sound of a letter, we mean the sound the letter stands for.

The letter **f** has the sound that you hear at the beginning of **feather**, in the middle of **coffee**, and at the end of **loaf**.

Some letters have only one sound, but many letters have more than one sound.

The letter **c** has one sound that is just like the sound of **k** in **kept**. Say **kind**, **carpet**, **calf**, **care**, and notice that all four words begin with the same sound. The sound of **c** in **carpet**, **calf**, and **care** is called the **hard sound of c**. You hear it in **caught**, **hiccups**, and **picnic**.

The letter **c** has another sound. It is the same as the sound of **s** in **silly**. Say **sent**, **city**, **certain**, and notice that all three words begin with the same sound. The sound of **c** in **city** and **certain** is called the **soft sound of c**. You can hear it in **cent**, **pencil**, and **ice**.

Say each of the following words. Decide whether the sound of the **c** is hard or soft.

calf   traffic   face   music   piece

130

The letter **g** has a soft sound and a hard sound. The soft sound is like the sound of **j** in **jump**. Notice that it is the first sound in **giraffe**, the middle sound in **magic**, and the last sound in **cage**.

The hard sound of **g** is the one you hear at the beginning of **goat**, in the middle of **ragged**, and at the end of **wag**.

In your reading you will sometimes find a new word that begins with **c** or **g**. Which sound, hard or soft, should you try first to find out whether it is a word you know?

If the second letter of the word is **e, i,** or **y**, try the soft sound of **c** or **g**. If the second letter is **a, o,** or **u**, try the hard sound of **c** or of **g**.

Read each question that follows, and think how to answer it:

What shape is a **circle**, round or square?

If you are at the **center** of a circle of children, are you inside the circle or outside the circle?

What size is a **giant**, very large or very small?

Young Tennessee and Old Sam

Young Tennessee lived all alone with his hound dog Ranger. He and that hound were about the best friends you could think of. They got along better than some people do.

They lived away out beyond the town where there were miles and miles of woods behind the open fields and very few people.

Young Tennessee thought living out there was all very nice, but sometimes he became curious about other places.

"You know, Ranger," he said to his hound dog one day, "there's a lot more to the world than what we can see from here. I think I'd like to take a look at it."

Next day Young Tennessee took his hound Ranger and went across the fields and through the woods to see Old Sam. Old Sam was the meanest, trickiest man around — or in the state or in the country, for that matter. He thought he was the smartest, too, but Young Tennessee went to see him anyway.

Young Tennessee knocked on the door. Pretty soon Old Sam opened the door just a crack and looked out. "Oh, it's you," he said. "Why don't you come in?"

"Because I want to get started," said Young Tennessee. "I'm planning to travel around and see the country."

Old Sam pushed the door almost tight shut. With one eye he looked through the narrow crack that was left and said, "I can't lend you a thing. I'm quite hard up myself — don't have any extra cash for you to spend traveling around the country."

"I don't expect you to lend me anything," said Young Tennessee. "I just want to know if you'll keep Ranger while I'm gone. I'll pay for his keep when I come back."

When Old Sam heard that, he opened the door up wide. "I guess I can keep that hound dog for you," he said.

The tricky old man had a hard time to keep from smiling. What a wonderful chance to get a hound dog free! Well, he would be smart enough to take it.

"Yes, I'll keep Ranger all right," he went on. "He'll be quite a lot of trouble, but I'll keep him. You take all the time you want to travel around and see the country."

So Young Tennessee left Ranger with Old Sam and traveled around the country.

He traveled to enough towns to find out that most towns look like other towns, and he slept in enough beds to find out that the easiest bed to sleep in was his own.

He spoke with enough people to find out that quite a lot of people don't like to lend things and will get something free instead of paying for it when they have the chance.

Finally he came back. He was tired, but he went right to Old Sam's house and knocked on the door.

After a long while Old Sam opened the door just a crack and called, "Who's there?"

"It's Young Tennessee. I'm through traveling around the country, and I've come for my dog Ranger."

Old Sam looked out through the narrow crack in the doorway.

"Oh, that hound dog!" he said.

"Yes," said Young Tennessee. "Where's Ranger?"

Old Sam didn't answer at once. He wasn't quite sure what to say. Finally he spoke.

"I'm really sorry to tell you the bad news, Young Tennessee, but your hound dog is no more.

"The first night after you left, I put Ranger in a stall in the old barn by the potato field. Well, what do you think? The potato bugs are so bad down there, they went in and ate up that hound dog."

Young Tennessee looked at Old Sam for a long time before he spoke.

Finally he said, "That's bad news, all right. And I'm in no shape to take bad news. I'm all tired out."

He was silent a while. Then he spoke again. "The potato bugs ate him, you say?"

Old Sam was so pleased at getting a free hound dog that he could hardly keep from laughing, but he said sadly, "I'm really sorry, Young Tennessee. I had no idea potato bugs would eat a hound dog."

Young Tennessee stood there quite a while longer. Finally he spoke up, "Well, I guess I might as well go along. But I wish you would do one little thing for me."

Old Sam was so happy about his free hound dog that he said, "That's not asking much. Can I lend you something perhaps?"

"Why, yes," said Young Tennessee. "Since you're so sorry the potato bugs ate Ranger, and I'm so tired out, suppose you lend me your mule to ride home on."

"My mule?" said Old Sam. "That's a good idea. I'll be glad to lend you my mule, free, but bring him back tomorrow."

But next day Young Tennessee didn't come back with the mule as he was supposed to. Old Sam waited for him and waited for him. Finally he couldn't stand it any longer. Just before night he hurried over to Young Tennessee's place and knocked hard on the door.

"Where's my mule?" he shouted.

Young Tennessee opened the door just a crack. "Your mule?" he said, softly and sadly.

"Well, I'm certainly sorry to tell you the bad news. I had that mule tied up in the field last night, and a big old owl came down, picked up that mule, and flew away with him. I had no idea an owl would do that."

"What!" cried out Old Sam. "You know good and well no big old owl could pick up a full-sized mule and fly away with him."

"Well," Young Tennessee said, "I was quite surprised myself. But let me tell you this: In a country where potato bugs eat hound dogs, anything can happen."

Old Sam stood and looked at Young Tennessee for a while. Finally he spoke.

"All right, if you think there's a chance you could find my mule, I have an idea that I might find your hound dog around somewhere."

And that's how Old Sam didn't get a free hound dog. For once he was tricked himself, instead of tricking somebody else.

Old-Time Peddlers

If you had lived long ago, you would probably have seen a man like the one in the picture. He is an old-time peddler. There aren't many peddlers of that kind traveling around now, but there were plenty of them years ago.

An old-time peddler had goods to sell. They were the kind of goods that stores sell, but the peddler had no store. He carried his goods in a pack on his back.

In those days people who lived a long way from a town or city didn't get to a store very often. Roads were not good. Wagons were hard to pull. Horses got tired. Of course there were no cars and no buses.

Most families were glad to have a peddler come along with his pack of goods. He might not have everything they needed, of course, but he was sure to have some things they could use.

The children of a family were often the first ones to see the peddler coming down the road. No matter what game they were playing, they stopped it and hurried to the house to see him open his pack.

And what a show it was! What colors! How many different things there were! Everyone was surprised that so many things could come out of a pack that one man could carry.

There might be five or six kinds of cloth. Some kinds would make dresses for Mother and the girls. Other kinds would make suits for Father and the boys.

There were sure to be gay tablecloths, and nearly always there were scissors, pins, and balls of string. Some peddlers carried small brooms, pans, cookie cutters, and other handy things for the kitchen.

A peddler always had something to catch the eyes of children. It might be pencils, games, tricks, whistles, tops, or other little toys. Once in a while he would have a music box that played lively music. Everyone liked that.

Of course most children would have liked to see their father and mother buy everything in the peddler's pack. No family did that, but almost every family did buy something.

When the family had bought what they wanted, the peddler packed up his goods and started off for the next house. Almost always he was a little happier when he left than he had been when he came, and the family was happy too because he had been there.

Nathan and the Peddler

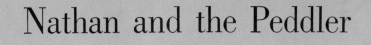

"Nathan Branch!" Mrs. Hodges shouted from the doorway of her house. "You're supposed to be digging potatoes. Why do you stand there looking up the road?"

"It's the peddler, Mrs. Hodges. See? Here he comes now." Nathan knew that he should keep on working, but he was eager to talk to the interesting man just now coming down the road. He was eager also for a chance to look at the wonderful things the peddler carried in his pack.

At the time Nathan lived, the peddler's coming was a very exciting happening in his town.

"Do you mean that Daniel Whitehill is here again?" asked Mrs. Hodges loudly. "Well, send him on his way!"

Nathan felt his face grow hot. He knew that the peddler must have heard her unkind words. But the peddler gave no sign that he had heard. He came walking along, leaning on his walking-stick because the pack on his back was so heavy.

Daniel stopped near Nathan and stood so that the heavy pack could rest on the gate post. "Good day!" he called politely to Mrs. Hodges. "Would you be interested to see what I have to sell today?"

"Indeed I would not!" answered the woman angrily. "I've no time to look at your goods and no wish to throw away my money."

The peddler's face did not change. He smiled at Nathan and said, "It's a fine sunny day for a boy's garden work."

"That it is," agreed Nathan.

The old man leaned on his walking-stick while he fixed the heavy bundle tightly on his back. Then he started off toward town.

Nathan looked back at Mrs. Hodges. She still stood in the doorway looking cross. As she turned and went into the house, Nathan suddenly decided to run after the peddler.

"Please, Mr. Whitehill," he said eagerly, "may I go with you as far as our field?"

"That you may," agreed Daniel, smiling. "Tell me your name."

"I'm Nathan. There's something I want to ask you. Is it really true that you travel as far as a hundred miles away? Perhaps even two hundred miles?"

The peddler nodded his head. "Even farther than that. I suppose I travel at least five hundred miles a year, from one part of the country to another."

"Then you've seen all the cities," said Nathan. "Have you seen Boston? I have a friend who went to Boston once."

"Yes," said the peddler, nodding his head. "I've seen Boston at least a hundred times."

"My friend told me that he saw the ocean when he went to Boston," said Nathan. "Have you seen the ocean, Mr. Whitehill?"

"That I have," answered the peddler. "I've watched great boats on the ocean, too."

"Someday I hope to travel," said Nathan, as he trudged along beside the peddler.

"What will your mother say to that?" asked the peddler. "Will she agree to it?"

"My mother isn't living, Mr. Whitehill," said Nathan sadly.

"Oh, I'm sorry to hear that," said Daniel. "Then Mrs. Hodges, is she — ?"

"Mrs. Hodges took me in when I had no home," said Nathan. "I don't really belong to her. The only one left in my family is a cousin, Mrs. Green. Mother used to tell me about her, but I've never seen her or heard from her."

The peddler nodded his head. "It's a hard thing for a boy to be alone in the world. But then, I guess all of us have our troubles."

"I guess so," Nathan agreed. "Well, here's the end of our field. I must go back now. I'll look for you, Mr. Whitehill, when you come this way again."

As Nathan trudged slowly back, he thought about the peddler and the wonderful way he lived. He tried to imagine how Boston and the ocean must look. He wished, as he had often wished before, that he could travel to visit his cousin, Mrs. Green.

When Nathan came into the kitchen, he found Mrs. Hodges at the stove. She was hot and tired and crosser than ever.

Nathan Has a Plan

"Nathan Branch!" she cried. "Who said you could visit with that no-good peddler? Go out to the barn and feed the cow."

As Nathan trudged off slowly, Mrs. Hodges called, "Bring back a pail of water. And full, mind you! None of your half-empty pails!"

"Yes, Mrs. Hodges," said Nathan.

Back he trudged for a pail. As he left again, Mrs. Hodges shouted, "And hurry! The woodbox is empty, and there's firewood to be chopped before you get any supper."

As Nathan trudged from one job to another, his mind was busy trying to imagine what a visit to Boston would be like. How wonderful the ocean and the big boats on the ocean must be! And over and over he thought of trying to find his cousin.

"It isn't the work I mind at this place," thought Nathan unhappily. "It's being scolded all the time. No matter how hard I try, I can never please Mrs. Hodges."

When Nathan finished his work and went into the house, Mrs. Hodges was halfway through eating her supper.

The table was very untidy. On one end was a pail of water. Close by were dirty dishes, empty cooking pans, and a dress which Mrs. Hodges had been sewing on.

There was only one pretty dish on the whole table. That was a beautiful silver salt dish. It was called "Standing Salt" because it stood on four carefully made feet.

"Standing Salt" had once belonged to Nathan's mother. When Mrs. Hodges took Nathan to live with her, she took the silver salt dish, too.

Nathan sat down quietly and began to eat. As he reached for a piece of bread, his arm knocked a pan against the silver salt dish and upset it. Mrs. Hodges began to scold at once.

"Nathan!" she cried. "Why can't you eat without knocking things over?"

She picked up the silver salt dish and found a scratch that the pan had made.

"Look!" she scolded angrily. "You've scratched my fine silver salt dish!"

Her scolding voice went on and on. The scolding was hard to stand, but it was her words, "*My* fine silver salt dish," that hurt Nathan most. He could see that she was planning to keep the one thing that he had set his heart on.

Suddenly Nathan jumped up and ran out of the house and down the road. He wanted to get away from Mrs. Hodges' scolding voice. He wanted to be where he would never again hear her call the silver salt dish hers. He started walking toward town.

Suddenly he thought of his friend John Wilder and decided to visit him. He could talk with John about Boston and the ocean. That would help him forget the scratched salt dish and Mrs. Hodges' scolding voice.

John's mother appeared at the door when Nathan knocked.

"Hello, Nathan!" she said. Her voice was soft and very friendly.

"I suppose you came to see John. I'm sorry he isn't here."

"He's gone away?" Nathan asked.

"Yes," said Mrs. Wilder. "His uncle from Boston came last night. He had to hurry back today. I decided to let John go along and make a visit to his cousins."

"Thank you," said Nathan. With a heavy heart he began the long trudge home.

It was late when Nathan got back from John's house, but Mrs. Hodges was waiting for him. As Nathan came into the yard, she appeared in the doorway, looking very cross.

"Where have you been?" she asked. "I've been looking for you all evening. You are a good-for-nothing boy. I wish I hadn't taken you in the first place. I wish you would go away and never come back!"

With that, she shut the door hard, leaving him outside in the yard.

Nathan went to the barn and lay down on his bed of hay near the cow.

But he didn't sleep. He just lay there on the hay, thinking of what had happened that day. Everything appeared to be going wrong.

Mrs. Hodges had been mean to the peddler. She had scolded Nathan for visiting with the peddler. She had scolded him when the silver salt dish was scratched, and she had called the beautiful dish hers.

When Nathan could stand her scolding voice no longer, he had tried to visit his good friend John. But John had gone away.

Finally he had heard Mrs. Hodges say in her scolding voice that she wished he would leave and never come back, and she had shut the door in his face.

"I wish I could go to Grantville to find my cousin, Mrs. Green," Nathan said to himself. "Perhaps she would let me live with her. It's a long way, but —"

Suddenly he sat up. A plan had flashed into his mind. "I know what I'll do," he told the cow. "Yes, I know just what to do." He lay back on the hay to think about his plan until at last he fell asleep.

Nathan Waits for the Peddler

The sun had not yet appeared the next morning when Nathan walked quietly through the yard to the woods. Then, like a flash, he ran through the woods and across a hayfield. There he stopped and looked up and down the road.

"Am I too late?" he asked himself. "Perhaps he has already left town."

Nathan lay down on a pile of hay to wait. After a long time Daniel Whitehill came trudging up the road, leaning on his strong walking-stick and carrying his heavy pack on his back. Nathan jumped up.

The peddler stopped suddenly. "Hello!" he cried. "It's young Nathan. Whatever brings you so far from home this early?"

"I — I've run away, Mr. Whitehill," said Nathan. "I'd like to go to Grantville with you, sir, to find my cousin, Mrs. Green."

The peddler looked surprised and then serious. He set his pack on the ground before he spoke. "Well, now, I wonder if you should," he said slowly. "Perhaps we'd better talk this over before we go on. Let's sit down on this pile of hay."

Nathan saw that Daniel's face was kind but serious.

"You don't appear to be hungry," said Daniel. "Didn't Mrs. Hodges feed you well?"

"Yes, sir," replied Nathan. "She let me have whatever was left on the table after she was through eating."

"Did you have a warm place to sleep?"

"Yes, sir. She let me sleep in the hay in the barn. But you see, Mrs. Hodges doesn't *like* me. She took me just because Doctor White told her to. And she keeps me because I work, so she doesn't have to pay a man to help on the place."

"Well, now, a boy should be willing to work for his keep," said the peddler, watching Nathan's face carefully.

"Oh, yes, sir," said Nathan seriously. "I don't mind the work. But she doesn't *like* me. Doctor White didn't say she had to like me. She scolds me all the time."

Nathan said nothing more for a while. Then he added, "I thought maybe you'd let me go along with you as far as Grantville, sir."

"Do you expect to live in Grantville with your cousin?" asked Daniel.

"Well," replied Nathan, "I plan to ask Cousin Abbie whether she'll let me stay with her. You could show me the way to Grantville, couldn't you, sir?"

"I could," said Daniel, "but I can't see my way clear to helping a boy run away. Appears to me you ought to find out whether Mrs. Hodges will agree to your leaving."

"She will agree," said Nathan. "She doesn't care whether I ever come back. She said she didn't want me in the first place and that I am good for nothing. She said so last night. She told me she wished I'd go away and never come back."

"Well, that makes it clear that she doesn't want you," said Daniel. "You're serious about going to your Cousin Abbie's in Grantville, are you?"

Nathan nodded his head.

"Well, I guess we won't have trouble finding the way," said Daniel.

"Then I may go with you?" asked Nathan.

The old man lifted his heavy pack to his back. "I enjoy having company when I'm trudging along with my pack," he said.

Side by side, the white-haired peddler and the boy went slowly down the road.

Suddenly Mr. Whitehill turned and asked, "Nathan, have you had any breakfast?"

"No, sir," replied Nathan. "I left before Mrs. Hodges woke up."

"I thought so," said the peddler. "Well, before we go any farther, we'll eat the johnnycake that Mrs. Post gave me today. It won't be a big meal, but you'll enjoy it."

When they had finished eating, Daniel lifted his pack to his back, and they went on.

Daniel stopped at every farm to trade. At first Nathan waited outside the farmhouses while the peddler did his trading, but when they came to a beautiful farmhouse about supper time, he changed his plan.

Three children came running through the front yard to meet them. "Company coming, Mother!" they shouted. "It's the peddler."

Daniel lifted his hat to the housewife waiting at the door. "Good evening, Mrs. Ellis," he called cheerfully.

"Well, now, I've been telling the children it was about time for a visit from Trader Whitehill," the woman said. "Come right in. We'd enjoy having you stay for supper."

"Thank you," said Daniel. "I want you to meet a good friend of mine. This boy Nathan is traveling along with me. He's going to visit a cousin of his."

"How do you do, Nathan?" said Mrs. Ellis. "Come in, both of you. Sit down while I lay two more places at the supper table."

After a hearty meal, everyone helped clear away the dishes. Then they all gathered around as the peddler got ready to open his pack. Nathan was as excited as the Ellis children. All day he had been eager to look at the interesting things inside the peddler's pack.

The children crowded around Daniel and leaned over to watch as he began to open his pack.

They were surprised to see how neatly and closely he had packed so many different things together.

There were handsome tablecloths, pretty dress goods, and yards and yards of bright-colored ribbons in neat rolls. There were kitchen pans, gay dishes, and boxes of spices. There were little heart-shaped cookie cutters and little glass bluebirds to use for salt dishes.

"Every housewife needs things for sewing," said Daniel cheerfully, as he showed needles, pins, and scissors to Mrs. Ellis.

"I don't suppose you have needles long enough to sew feed bags," said Mr. Ellis.

"Yes, indeed," said Daniel. "There are some needles just the right length, I think."

Mrs. Ellis chose some cloth for dresses, two papers of needles, and two boxes of spices. The children chose a heart-shaped cookie cutter and some glass bluebirds.

Mr. Ellis chose some big needles that were the right length for sewing up feed bags. Then he gave Daniel the money to pay for the things the family had bought.

"Thank you for this real money," said Daniel. "Most people try to trade things for what they have bought. Often after I have cut off a length of cloth, I am asked to take a bag of potatoes, a pig, or something like that for pay. I don't mind trading small things, but how could I carry a pig?"

That night, as Nathan lay beside Daniel on a feather bed in the kitchen, he thought over the events of the last two days and wondered anxiously about the events ahead.

Suppose he couldn't find Cousin Abbie? Suppose she wouldn't let him live with her? Then he thought of the kind and wise peddler who lay beside him. Soon he forgot all his problems and fell asleep.

Good News for Nathan

For several weeks Nathan and the peddler walked from town to town, stopping at every farmhouse to trade. Nearly everyone was anxious to buy something. While Daniel was trading with a farmer and his wife, Nathan made himself useful chopping wood, getting water, and doing other things.

Nathan enjoyed traveling with Daniel. A peddler's life was all he had imagined it would be. They were free to go wherever they chose to go. It was always fun to guess what events the next day would bring.

Would they get to a farmhouse at meal time and be asked to have a meal with the family? Or would they go hungry for half a day or more because houses were too far apart? Where would they sleep? On a feather bed in an inn or on a bed of hay in a barn?

One morning the two travelers were going down a wide country road. Some men on horseback rode by. Soon several riders and some heavy wagons passed them. The road seemed crowded to Nathan.

"I never saw such a busy road in all my life," he said. "Where do you suppose all the people are going?"

"To Traders' Point, I think," said Daniel. "We'll get there this afternoon and stay at the inn tonight."

"Is Traders' Point a city?" Nathan asked.

"No," replied Daniel. "It's just a town, but it's a good place to trade. I'll sell the things people have traded for my goods. That will make my heavy pack lighter."

At noon they came to the top of a hill and looked down on Traders' Point.

"There!" said Daniel. "How does it look?"

"Wonderful!" answered Nathan. "It's the biggest town I've seen in all my life."

Soon the travelers were standing in front of a two-room house. A sign in a window said, MRS. PATCH, BAKED GOODS.

The peddler pushed open the door of the shop, making a bell ring.

"Good afternoon!" he called heartily.

A little old woman popped out of the room at the back of the shop.

"Daniel Whitehill!" she exclaimed. "I'm glad to see you. I hope you brought plenty of spices. I can't say which makes me happier, seeing you or getting spices."

"Both, I hope," said Daniel cheerfully, as he lifted the heavy pack from his back. "And now what have you for hungry travelers? Good cooking I may find elsewhere, but no one else knows your baking tricks. The wonderful smell of this bake shop would make a wooden Indian's mouth water."

"I'll get some spice cake and some cookies," said Mrs. Patch. "Sit down."

She pointed to stools at the table.

Mrs. Patch smiled at Nathan as he sat down on a stool. "I know you must be hungry," she said. "I'll give you cold buttermilk to drink with your cookies."

"Nathan's helping me," Mr. Whitehill explained, as Mrs. Patch brought in glasses of buttermilk. "He's making a trip to Grantville to visit a cousin of his."

Mrs. Patch nodded, but Nathan wondered whether she had heard. She seemed too busy setting the table and cutting spice cake to listen to anybody.

When they had finished eating, the peddler and Mrs. Patch had a long talk. Finally Daniel said, "Nathan, would you like to stay here in the shop this afternoon while I make my rounds in Traders' Point?"

"If I can help Mrs. Patch," said Nathan, "I'd like to show her my thanks."

"That you can!" exclaimed Mrs. Patch. "I've had no help in shop or kitchen since my daughter left home several months ago."

So during the afternoon Nathan helped around the bake shop while Mrs. Patch made pies. She enjoyed talking with Nathan and explained at great length the events and life in the town. From all that she said, Nathan felt sure that it must be wonderful to live in such a busy place.

Nathan and Daniel had their evening meal with Mrs. Patch. Later, as the boy and the peddler walked together toward the inn, Daniel said, "Mrs. Patch is a fine lady, and she likes you very much, Nathan."

"I like her too," replied Nathan.

"She asked me a question I couldn't answer," went on the old man. "She wanted to know whether you would give up your trip to Grantville and stay in Traders' Point with her, for keeps.

"She'd give you your meals, a home, and some money in return for your help around the shop. She's a wonderful lady. It's something to think about."

"No one ever wanted me around before just because she liked me," said Nathan.

"I enjoy having you around," the peddler said, "but it appears to me that Mrs. Patch has something especially fine for you. She'd let you go to school when she could. And as for this cousin of yours, we don't really know whether she'll have room —"

"Or whether she'll want me," said Nathan.

"Well, you think it over," said the peddler, as they neared the inn.

Nathan was happier than he had ever imagined he would be. To be wanted, that was the most important thing in his life.

But as Nathan looked through the doorway into the inn, his happiness was suddenly taken from him. For there, leaning against the fireplace and talking seriously with the innkeeper, was Doctor White from Nathan's town!

Nathan took hold of the peddler's arm. "I can't go in there!" he exclaimed. "That important-looking man is Doctor White! Do you think Mrs. Hodges sent him after me?"

"That man leaning against the fireplace?" asked the peddler. "Why should a busy doctor travel a hundred miles across the country especially to chase a runaway boy?"

"He's the man who got Mrs. Hodges to take me in," Nathan explained. "Do you think he came after me?"

The peddler shook his head. "I wouldn't know," he said. "But suppose you go back to Mrs. Patch. She'll give you a place to sleep for tonight. I'll stay here at the inn and talk with this doctor. Tomorrow morning I'll tell you what I've learned."

Nathan slept little that night. Early in the morning Mr. Whitehill appeared at the bake shop. "Good morning, Nathan," he said cheerfully. "And it *is* a good morning, because the news I have will bring you happiness.

"Doctor White came to Traders' Point especially to visit a patient. He did not know that you had left Mrs. Hodges, but he said he was glad you did. It appears that he has come to know Mrs. Hodges better, and he realizes now that she is not the kind of woman to bring up a young boy."

"That is good news," said Nathan. "But I think that I should go on with you to find my Cousin Abbie in Grantville. I realize that Mrs. Patch really wants me to stay, but I am anxious to meet Cousin Abbie."

Mrs. Patch had come into her kitchen while Nathan was speaking. She said sadly, "Go to your cousin's, then. But it does seem to me that she's not a very good cousin if she didn't send for you or at least try to help you when you needed her."

"Now, Mrs. Patch," said Daniel. "This cousin of Nathan's has never seen him, and of course she doesn't realize that the boy has had such an unhappy life."

Mrs. Patch shook Nathan's hand. "All right," she said, "but mind that you come straight back to me if your cousin in Grantville can't or won't take you in."

"Thank you, Mrs. Patch," said Nathan. "I'll be glad to."

Day after day Nathan and the peddler trudged on. The trip to Grantville was taking longer than Nathan had imagined it would. One day he decided to speak to the peddler about it.

"When will we get to Grantville?" he asked somewhat anxiously.

"We're going straight toward it," Daniel explained. "We're more than halfway now. Of course you are anxious to meet your cousin, but you know a peddler can't hurry."

"Oh, yes, sir, I know that," replied Nathan. "You have a lot of trading to do, and I want to help you. I can be patient. I can wait to meet Cousin Abbie."

Fall came and brought shorter days, longer nights, and icy mornings. There were stormy days that brought rain and snow. Traveling wasn't so easy now. Yet Nathan was happy if he could warm himself by a kitchen fire before breakfast. He was especially glad to sit by a cheerful fire in the evening.

One night the travelers slept in a barn. The next morning they woke up early. Nathan was cold and hungry. As he lay on his bed of hay, feeling sorry for himself, Mr. Burns, the farmer, opened the barn door.

"Mr. Whitehill!" he called in a cheerful voice. "You and the boy come up to the house for breakfast."

The travelers hurried across the barnyard and into the kitchen.

"You must be cold," said Mrs. Burns. "Sit down on these stools by the stove and have a dish of hot oatmeal. I'll soon have pancakes, toast, and eggs for you."

"You are up early," said Daniel.

"Yes," said Mr. Burns. "We have planned a trip of several miles for today. A neighbor is having a house raising on a piece of land that he has cleared. He wants to get the house up before another rain storm comes."

"A house raising is an important event in our life," explained Mrs. Burns.

"I imagine that neighbors from farms far and near will gather there," said Daniel.

"People come from town, too," said Mr. Burns. "They enjoy events like house raisings."

"Nathan, don't you think we'd better go along to this house raising?" the peddler asked. "I'm too old to do any climbing or heavy lifting, but I can do some jobs."

Nathan nodded eagerly. When the morning work was finished, Mr. and Mrs. Burns started off on a narrow road through the woods. Daniel and Nathan followed.

After a while they heard sounds of chopping and sawing. Then they began to hear voices. Soon they reached the clearing.

About half a hundred people were there, and more and more neighbors kept coming. Little children ran about gathering firewood for cooking the noon meal. Boys carried pails of cold water to the house builders. Girls took care of babies and helped the women cook for the large crowd.

Nathan was eager to help with the house raising, too. He decided to help the men who were building the stone fireplace. The biggest stones were too heavy for him to lift, but he rolled smaller stones from a pile at the side of the clearing.

There were several boys at the house raising. Nathan noticed that one of them was about his own age. That boy smiled at Nathan and came over to speak to him.

"My name is Robert," he said. "Are you one of our new neighbors?"

Nathan shook his head. "No, I came with Mr. Whitehill, the peddler," he explained. "My name is Nathan."

"I know who the peddler is," said Robert. "He just went over there to speak to my mother." He pointed across the clearing.

Nathan had already noticed that Daniel was talking seriously with a kind-faced lady who was cooking something over a fire.

"It must be fun to go with a peddler," Robert said. "I'd like to travel over the country and visit important places. Have you ever seen Boston and the ocean?"

Nathan shook his head. "Not yet," he said, "but I want to someday."

"Well, I must go to help my father," said Robert. "Let's eat dinner together. Then you can tell me all about a peddler's life. Will you?"

Nathan nodded.

With a friendly wave of his hand, Robert ran off, and Nathan returned to his stone rolling, more cheerful than he had been for a long time. Robert was the first friend his own age that Nathan had made since John had gone away.

Nathan was happy. He didn't seem to realize that the stones were heavy. He didn't notice that Daniel was near until he heard him speak.

"Take it easy, boy," he heard Daniel say. "You can't pile all the stones by yourself. Come and sit down. I have something to tell you."

They sat down on a large stone and leaned against a tree. Nathan waited anxiously for Daniel to begin to speak.

"Do you realize that Grantville is not far from here?" Daniel asked quietly.

"Really!" Nathan exclaimed. He could hardly realize that it was true. For two months they had been traveling toward that town but it never seemed any nearer.

"Yes, really," replied Daniel. "It is the next town on the road. Half of Grantville must have come to this house raising. The cousin you are so anxious to meet is here."

"Cousin Abbie Green?" exclaimed Nathan.

"Just across the clearing," said Daniel. "I have been talking with her."

"Robert and I saw you," said Nathan. "That lady is his mother. He's just my age."

"Yes, she has a boy your age and two little girls," explained the peddler. "I want you to go and meet them now."

Mrs. Green didn't see Daniel and Nathan as they came across the clearing. She was leaning over, putting wood on the fire and watching things that were cooking.

"Mrs. Green, here is Nathan," Daniel said.

At the sound of his voice, she straightened up, turned, and smiled at Nathan.

"Cousin Nathan!" she exclaimed as she shook hands with him warmly. "How much like your mother you look! She and I were little girls together in Grantville years ago. It makes me sad to realize that she is gone."

Nathan was too excited to speak.

"Your mother and I got out of touch with each other after she moved away," explained Mrs. Green. "I didn't even know she had a son. If I had realized you needed a home, of course I'd have sent for you long ago."

"I imagine that Mrs. Hodges knew Nathan had a cousin," said the peddler.

"Oh, yes, sir, she did," said Nathan. "Once she promised to write to Cousin Abbie."

Robert came running up just then and pulled Nathan away. "Now tell me what life with a peddler is like," he said eagerly.

Nathan ate his noon meal with Robert and his sisters. They made him talk at great length about his life with Mr. Whitehill and the interesting places he had seen.

Just before the house raising was finished, Daniel had a talk with Nathan.

"Your cousin Abbie tells me you are going to live with her," he said. "You'll get along well with a lady like her."

"Yes, sir," replied Nathan. "She says I'm to be just another son. It will be fine to have a family of my own and a brother my own age like Robert. I can go to school with Robert, too. I'll like that."

The peddler nodded his head. "Of course you'll like school," he said. "And it's especially fine that you'll have a real home."

Nathan did not reply. Daniel turned to look at him. "What's the trouble, my boy? Everything has turned out the way we wanted it to, and yet you look so serious. Speak up. What's the matter?"

Nathan looked down at the ground. "Well, you see, sir, I've been thinking about you and how good you've been to me. When you travel on, Mr. Whitehill, you'll be all alone." Nathan was having trouble speaking his mind, but he went on.

"Don't you think you'll need me, sir? I'll miss you, Mr. Whitehill."

The peddler laughed. "I enjoy your company, too, boy," he said. "So I've decided to spend the winter in Grantville."

"Oh, Mr. Whitehill!" Nathan exclaimed. "Really? I'm so glad to hear that."

"Yes," the old man went on, "winter isn't a good time to be traveling and peddling. So I'll spend the cold winter months shoeing horses, fixing pans and shoes, and — oh, Nathan, you don't realize half the jobs I can do."

Just then a boy's voice sounded across the clearing. "Nathan! Nathan!"

"It's Robert," Nathan said, jumping to his feet. "There are to be some running races now for boys our age, and he wants me to run."

Nathan's heart was light as he waved to the peddler and ran quickly across the clearing. He was really happy now, for at last he had found a home and family.

And, added to this happiness, he would still be near his old friend, the peddler.

Vowel Sounds

The five letters **a, e, i, o,** and **u** are called **vowels**. The sounds that they stand for are called **vowel sounds**.

Every vowel has several sounds.

Read the following sentence softly to yourself, and listen to hear the different sounds of **a** in the words printed in very black letters. If you read it correctly, you can hear five different sounds of **a.**

Every **day** when we were **at** the **farm** we **ate all** the ripe **apples** we **cared** for.

In which word, or words, in the sentence does **a** sound like **a** in **save**? Like **a** in **square**? Like **a** in **glad**? Like **a** in **large**? Like **a** in **stalls**?

Listen to hear three different sounds of **e** as you read this sentence clearly:

She feeds fresh eggs to **her pets.**

In which of the words does **e** sound like **e** in **get**? Like **e** in **farmer**? Like the first **e** in **these**?

Read the following sentence and listen for three different vowel sounds of **i:**

The **first five fish Bill** caught were just the **right size** for a **birthday dinner**.

In which words does the **i** sound like **i** in **milk**? Like **i** in **third**? Like **i** in **fire**?

Read this sentence aloud correctly, and hear four different sounds of the vowel **o**:

Bob put a big **box** at the **corner of** the **front** steps, **covered** it with an **old robe**, and called it a **home for monkeys**.

In which words does the **o** sound like **o** in **lot**? Like **o** in **broken**? Like **o** in **horse**? Like **o** in **done**?

Find three sounds of **u** in the words in the following sentences:

Last **Thursday** we were **surely lucky**. A **hurdy-gurdy** man came by **during** the **music** time and played five **numbers**.

In which words does **u** sound like **u** in **bundle**? Like **u** in **purple**? Like **u** in **use**?

Two words may look just alike but have different vowel sounds and meanings. Use the sound giving the right meaning:

If the **wind** gets to blowing any harder, you had better **wind** up your kite string.

You know that the letters **a** , **e** , **i** , **o** , and **u** are called **vowels** .

What are the vowels in the word **report** ?

Say **report** softly to yourself and notice that you say it in two parts, **re port** . What vowel sound is in the first part, **re** ? What vowel sound is in the last part, **port** ?

The two parts of the word **report** are called **syllables** . The first syllable is **re** ; the second syllable is **port** . Notice that in each syllable there is a vowel sound.

Each of the following words has two syllables. Say each word so clearly that you hear the two syllables and the vowel sound in each syllable.

traffic	**zebra**	**under**	**correct**
after	**event**	**carpet**	**mayor**
music	**paper**	**nickel**	**coming**

Say the word **motorman** and notice that you hear three parts, **mo tor man** . How many syllables does **motorman** have? How many vowel sounds? What are they?

Say each of the following words and decide how many syllables it has:

shadow	flash	happiness	even
important	lady	hiccups	trip
test	batter	elephant	expect
violet	wand	interesting	excited

In which words did you hear just one vowel sound? Which words have only one syllable?

In which words did you hear two vowel sounds? Which words have two syllables?

In which words did you hear three vowel sounds? Which words have three syllables?

Which of the words has four syllables?

Many words have only one syllable. The word **wag** is a one-syllable word. Say **wag** and notice that you hear only one part and only one vowel sound.

Say these one-syllable words:

scratch	length	lift	hind	wet
mumps	lend	bent	bug	dig

What vowel sound do you hear in each word?

A word may have more than one vowel and yet have only one syllable. How many vowels are in each of these five words?

save   these   ripe   robe   mule

Say the five words. How many vowel sounds do you hear in each word?

There are two vowels in each of the words but only one vowel sound. So each of these words has just one syllable.

How many syllables are there in each of these words?

pile   pie   hose   cage   sister
chose   bridge   police   women   kite

Sometimes a one-syllable word has two vowels that stand side by side, but only one of the vowels is sounded. Say each of these one-syllable words and decide what vowel sound you hear:

fruit   leap   fourth   coach   raise
great   friend   piece   cries   straight
nail   least   cream   beard   build

In which of the words is the first vowel the one that is sounded? In which words is it the second vowel?

There are many one-syllable words in which two vowels stand side by side. If you find a strange word that looks as if it might be that kind, try using the sounds of the first vowel when you say it. If that doesn't make a word you know, try using the sounds of the second vowel.

Always remember that the word must make sense in what you are reading.

In the sentence that follows there are two new one-syllable words printed in very black letters. Use what you have learned about vowel sounds to help you read them.

Ever since Tom learned to **float**, he has enjoyed going to the **beach**.

Sometimes **y** is used as a vowel. In words like **cry**, **why**, **fly**, **y** has the same sound as long **i** in **spice**. In words like **empty**, **lucky**, **lady**, **y** has the same sound as short **i** in **sit**. Often **y** is silent as in **gray**.

How many syllables has each of these words?

carry   tricky   monkey   hurdy-gurdy

Just for Fun

Mr. See and Mr. Saw went fishing one day. They found a place where they caught a lot of fish.

"Let's make a mark on the boat to help us find this place again," said Mr. Saw.

"That's silly," said Mr. See. "How do we know that we'll come in the same boat next time?"

A man riding horseback saw a little dog trotting along the road.

"Good morning," said the dog.

"Good morning," said the man.

As the dog went on down the road, the man said, "I didn't know dogs could talk."

"I didn't either," said the horse.

SILLY SAM: What has six feet, green eyes, and a purple body with yellow stripes?

TOM: I don't know. What?

SILLY SAM: I don't know either, but you had better pick it off your neck.

One night Mr. Saw saw Mr. See looking for something under a streetlight.

"What are you looking for?" asked Mr. Saw.

"I've dropped a nickel," said Mr. See.

Mr. Saw helped Mr. See look for the nickel for some time. They didn't find it. At last Mr. Saw asked, "Just where did you drop the nickel, Mr. See?"

"Up the street," replied Mr. See.

"Then why are you looking here for it?" asked Mr. Saw.

"The light's better here," said Mr. See.

Lighthouses

When ships come near land, they are always in danger of running onto rocks or getting into water that is not deep enough for them.

Sailors cannot keep their ships away from such dangers if they do not know where the dangers are.

Such places have to be marked in some way that can be seen from the ships while they are still far away from trouble. Big ships can not be stopped quickly.

Long ago men began to build lighthouses to mark places of great danger along the shores of oceans, seas, and lakes. No one knows when or where the first one was built, but now there are hundreds of lighthouses along rocky shores in all parts of the world.

Some lighthouses are built on rocky islands. Some stand on hills near the shore. Some are built on points of land that stick out into the water. They are always built where they can be seen from ships that are still many miles from them.

Most lighthouses are round, high buildings. Most of them are wider at the bottom than at the top. Nearly all lighthouses are painted white so that they can be seen easily in daytime by ships that are far from shore.

Every lighthouse is shaped or painted or marked in some way that makes it appear different in daylight from other lighthouses near it. A few are built with four sides, and some are built with six sides. Some have black bands or wide stripes painted on them.

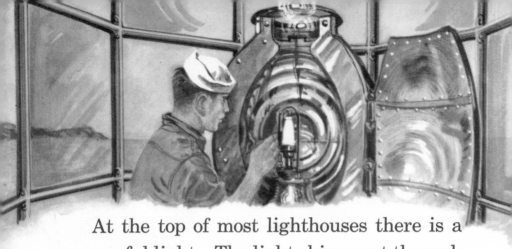

At the top of most lighthouses there is a powerful light. The light shines out through a special kind of window which is built so that it turns around and around the light. As the window turns, it makes the light appear to flash on and off.

The lights that flash from the lamp rooms of lighthouses are different from one another. The colors of the lights or the length of the flashes may be different.

Sailors very quickly learn to know one lighthouse from another. When they see a lighthouse in the daytime or its flashing light at night, they know just where their ship is.

So, by day and by night, lighthouses warn sailors of dangers and help them bring their ships safely into harbors.

A hundred years ago, many of the lamps used in lighthouses were oil lamps. The part of the lamp that was lighted was called the wick. At the top of the lamp at the right you see a wick.

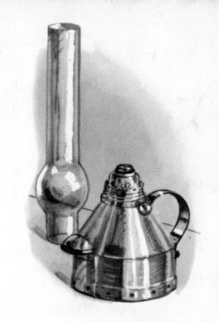

One end of the wick was in the oil at the bottom of the lamp. The other end was up where the lamp was lighted. The oil came up slowly through the wick.

It wasn't much trouble for the lightkeeper to touch a match to the top of the wick when an oil lamp was to be lighted, but it took a lot of work to get an oil lamp ready.

Every lightkeeper wanted his lamp to give a bright light. So every day he made sure that there was enough oil in the lamp. He cleaned the wick and made it even at the top. He cleaned all the glass around the lamp so that the warning light could shine through bright and clear.

When a fog covers the shore of the ocean or of a lake, a lighthouse is no help in warning ships of danger there. Fogs are often so heavy that sailors cannot see the lighthouse or the flashing lights at all.

At such times, lightkeepers use foghorns to warn ships of danger. A powerful foghorn can be heard several miles out at sea when the wind is right.

Fog often comes in suddenly and when it is least expected. But whenever it comes, the foghorn must be started and kept going until the fog clears away. In lighthouses of today that is easy. Turning on a foghorn is no harder than turning on a light.

A hundred years ago there were very few foghorns to warn sailors when fogs came in. When a lightkeeper had no foghorn, he had to ring a big bell by pulling a heavy rope. He had to ring the bell until the fog cleared.

Along the shores of oceans, seas, and lakes, ships are traveling every day and every night. They travel safely because they can use lighthouses as landmarks.

Keeping a lighthouse now is not such hard work as it was a hundred years ago when wicks, oil lamps, and fog bells were used. But the job is as important as ever.

All day and all night, in summer and in winter, through rain, snow, wind, and fog, the lighthouses and their keepers are on the job. By their warnings of danger, they help save the lives of hundreds of people and bring ships safely into their harbors.

Sally Finds a Way

Years ago a little girl named Sally lived with her father in a lighthouse. Her father was the lightkeeper there.

Sally's father had an oil lamp to take care of. Every day he shined the glass around the lamp, filled the lamp with oil, and cleaned the wick carefully. Every night he lighted the lamp with a match.

The lighthouse had no foghorn. When the fog rolled in, the keeper had to ring the big fog bell that was outside the lighthouse and keep ringing it until the fog cleared.

Sally's father had explained to her many times how important the light and the fog bell were. She knew how they warned sailors to keep their ships away from the rocks on which the lighthouse stood.

Sally liked to watch her father light the lamp. She often climbed with him to the top of the lighthouse. Sometimes he held her up and let her touch the wick with the lighted match.

But Sally's father never let her ring the fog bell. He said that pulling the bell rope was a man's work, because the rope and the bell were so heavy.

Sally had no mother and no brothers or sisters to play with. But she found plenty of things to do. She followed her father about as he worked, helped him with the housework, and played with her little kitten, Pitter. She had a few books, too, and could read very well.

Every afternoon the Boston boat came into the harbor. Sally liked to wave to the sailors. Sometimes the sailors waved to her. The thing Sally especially wanted to do was to ride on the boat to Boston and back.

The lighthouse was on a rocky point of land across the harbor from a town. When Sally's father needed groceries or clothes, he went in his boat across the harbor to the town. Sometimes he took Sally with him.

One day at noon he said, "Sally, we need some food. I'm making a trip to town to buy some fruit and vegetables, a loaf or two of bread, and some milk. I need some nails, too.

"While I'm in town, I'll stop at the post office and pick up our mail. Can you think of anything else we need?"

"No, I guess not," said Sally, "except — do they have candy and sweet crackers in the grocery store?"

Sally's father laughed. "They might have," he said. "I'll see."

"I wish you could take me," said Sally. She wanted very much to go.

"I wish I could, too," said her father, "but I expect our small boat will be so full when I come home that there will be room just for me. I want to make a quick trip. I mustn't be away from the lighthouse very long.

"You can be the housekeeper this afternoon. Wash the dishes and clean up the carpet in the living room. Then you can play outdoors a while. Before you know it, I'll be home again."

"All right," said Sally.

"I think I'd better go along now," said her father. "I want to be sure to be back before it's time to light the lamp."

Father went off in his boat. Sally waved her hand as long as she could see him. Then she went to work.

She washed the dishes and put them away. She got out the broom and cleaned the kitchen floor and the living room carpet. She put the furniture in place. Then her housekeeping work was done.

She took Pitter, the little kitten, out on the sandy shore near the water. The sun was shining bright. It was a beautiful day. She tried to teach Pitter to chase little round stones, but Pitter seemed to think it was more fun to chase his tail or chase the little bugs that he imagined he saw.

After a while Sally went into the house again. She decided to make gingerbread for supper. She put on her white ruffled apron, made the batter, put it in a pan, and put the pan in the oven.

When the gingerbread was done, Sally went outdoors to see whether her father was coming yet in the boat.

She was surprised to find that the day was no longer bright. The sun wasn't shining now. The wind was blowing hard, and the waves were high. The ocean was covered with whitecaps.

"I wish Father would come home," she said to herself. "A storm is coming up, and if he doesn't hurry he won't be able to get here before dark."

Indeed, it became darker and darker as Sally stood outside. The wind was blowing harder than ever now. Great waves came rolling in. When they broke against the rocks, the noise they made was very loud.

Sally soon realized that her father would not be able to get home until the storm was over. It would not be safe for him to come in his small boat.

She felt a little frightened. She ran into the lighthouse and shut all the windows just as it began to rain.

It was so dark now that Sally had to light the little lamp in the kitchen. Suddenly she realized that though it wasn't yet night, it was so dark that sailors wouldn't be able to see the lighthouse or the rocks.

She realized, too, that it was almost time for the Boston boat to be coming into the harbor. There should be a light to warn the sailors away from the rocks.

"The big lamp must be lighted," said Sally to herself. "I'm not sure I can do it, but I must try."

She lighted a small oil lamp. With the lamp and some matches, she started up the long stairway that went round and round until it reached the top of the lighthouse.

At last she came to the room at the top of the stairway. She set the little lamp down. Then she stretched up her hand to turn up the wick of the big lamp, but she found that she was too short to reach it.

"I'll have to get something to stand on," she said.

Down the long stairway she went again. This time she brought a footstool and climbed up on it. Still she couldn't reach the big lamp.

"I'll get a box," she said to herself, and down the stairs she went again. Up she came with a wooden box. This time she could reach the big lamp.

She turned up the wick and carefully cleaned off the black, burned part, as she had seen her father do. Then she lighted the lamp.

When she had closed the glass cover and saw the lamp shining clear and bright, she felt very proud of herself.

"Now the sailors on the Boston boat can find their way safely into the harbor," she thought. "And the light will show Father the way home, too."

She went down the long stairway, feeling very happy and proud.

When she was downstairs, she could tell from the sound of the rain on the windows that it was not raining so hard as it had been. The wind had almost stopped blowing, too. But it still seemed dark.

"The storm is almost over," Sally thought, "but it seems to be darker than ever outside. I wonder why."

Fog!

She went outdoors to look again for her father, and then she knew why it seemed so dark. A heavy fog had rolled in from the ocean. It covered the harbor, the land, and the rocks. Sally had seen fog many times, but it wasn't often so heavy as this.

She looked up at the light, and her heart leaped wildly. She could hardly see the light from where she stood. The sailors on the Boston boat wouldn't be able to see it at all. And her father surely couldn't see it from the other side of the harbor.

What should she do now?

"The fog bell!" thought Sally. "Father always rings the fog bell when the fog is too heavy for the light to shine through it."

Then she remembered that her father had always told her that ringing the fog bell was a man's work. The bell was big and heavy, and so was the rope. But Sally knew that someone had to ring the bell, and she was the only one to do it.

The fog bell was on the outside of the lighthouse. The rope that pulled it came in through a small hole in the side of the lighthouse. The end of the rope was at the bottom of the stairway that went up to the lightroom.

Sally took hold of the heavy bell rope and began to pull. Nothing happened. She tried again to pull the rope, but still the fog bell would not ring.

She was almost ready to cry. If she couldn't ring the bell, the Boston boat might run onto the rocks, and the sailors would be drowned.

Then she thought, "Perhaps if I walk a little way up the stairs, take hold of the rope, and then walk down holding it, that will make the bell ring. I'll try it."

She went up a few steps, and then took hold of the bell rope. She held it tight in both hands and walked down the stairs. Her idea was a good one. When she reached the bottom of the stairs, the fog bell clanged loudly.

Sally walked up the few steps a second time, and the bell clanged again. Down the stairs she came, and again the bell clanged. Soon the bell was ringing out loud and clear.

It wasn't long before Sally began to feel very tired. The rope hurt her hands, and her arms were so tired that they felt as though they would drop right off. Her legs hurt from climbing up and down the stairs. But she kept on ringing the bell by walking up and down the first few steps.

When Sally's father heard the fog bell, he started home at once in his little boat. So that the boat would be easy to handle, he left behind some of the groceries he had bought. He headed the boat for the lighthouse and went as fast as he could go.

But even though he went as fast as he could, it still took him a long time to cross the harbor. When he reached the point of land where the lighthouse stood, he quickly pulled his boat up on the narrow sandy shore and ran into the lighthouse.

There at the bottom of the stairs was Sally, with the bell rope held tight in her hands.

"Daddy!" cried Sally, almost in tears. "I'm so glad you've come. I couldn't climb up those steps one more time."

Sally didn't know when her father carried her into her bedroom and put her to bed, because she was asleep in half a second. She didn't hear the fog bell ringing far into the night, and she didn't know when the fog finally cleared away and her father stopped ringing the fog bell.

The next day Sally's arms and legs hurt a little, but she knew that they would feel all right in a few days. In the afternoon she and her father took the boat and went across the harbor to town to get the groceries that her father had left behind the day before.

While they were there, they happened to meet a sailor from the Boston boat. He knew Sally's father.

"It was lucky for us that you were at the lighthouse to ring that fog bell and warn us away from the rocks," the sailor told Sally's father. "If you hadn't started to ring the bell when you did, we might not be here now. Our ship was pretty close to the rocks when the bell began to ring."

"Oh, but I didn't ring the bell," said Sally's father. "That was my little girl." And he explained what had happened.

"You're a daughter to be proud of, all right," said the sailor to Sally. "I guess you saved my life and a good many others last night.

"I don't know what to say, except thank you. But maybe I can do something for you. Perhaps I can fix things so that you go to Boston with us on our next trip. How would you like that?"

Sally was too happy to speak. Her voice wouldn't come out. But she did whisper, "Oh, I'd like it, thank you."

You can be sure that Sally was on the boat the next time it went to Boston.

Now and Then

The Magic Shoes

No one would ever have thought that the little shoes were magic shoes. They were small and strong and looked much like any other good pair of shoes for a boy.

Any boy who looked at the shoes would have known that it would take a long time to wear them out, but he would not have known that they were magic shoes. He could not have found out what they would do or how they would feel until he put them on.

It is true that they were not quite plain. They did have shining copper bands across the square toes and around the heels. But other shoes had square copper toes and copper heels. It wasn't the copper that put magic into the shoes.

But the magic was there, and everybody who got to wear the shoes found that out.

It all began when a young mother's first son was born. All the neighbors came to see what the newborn baby's fairy godmother would bring him. Some guessed it would be a bag of gold. Others thought it would be a golden cup set with costly stones.

When the fairy godmother arrived, she held a small box in her hand.

"My dear," she said to the young mother, " this is just an everyday kind of present, but I am quite sure it will be useful.

"We fairies have found out that it isn't wise to give either beautiful things or costly things to children, for they never know what to do with either kind."

The box was opened, and the godmother gave to the young mother — *a small pair of strong shoes with copper toes and heels.*

"These shoes are made of magic leather," said the fairy godmother. "Little feet can never wear them out. Each son or daughter that is born to you will step into these shoes just when his or her little feet are old enough to wander."

The neighbors were surprised that the fairy godmother had brought such a small gift, but the young mother took the shoes and thanked the godmother for them.

"If your children are as wise as you are, they will need nothing a fairy can give them," said the fairy godmother.

"But all the same, my little gift is not quite so small as it looks. I told you that little feet cannot wear out these shoes. Little feet cannot very easily wander in them, either. The shoes will take your first-born son to school, bring him straight home after school, and —

"Well, as the years go by, you will find out the good things about these little leather shoes. Each of the children born to you can take his turn wearing them."

As the years went by and ten sons were born, the mother learned how useful the fairy godmother's gift really was.

Each boy, in turn, wore the little leather shoes with the copper heels and toes. He put them on when his feet were just big enough to wander and wore them until his feet were too big to wander any more.

As long as a boy wore the magic gift, he was quite sure to go where he was sent and to come back when he was supposed to. That is a good habit, as mothers know. But it is no easy matter to get children to learn it.

Moreover, during the time that each boy wore the shoes, the good habit became so strong that he was quite well behaved after he was through wearing them. That made the gift even more wonderful.

Everything went well until it was time for the last-born son to get the shoes. He had to wait, of course, for the next to the last brother to stop wearing them. But that brother had small feet. He wore the shoes longer than his big brothers had worn them.

Timothy, the youngest son, should have had the shoes sooner. His feet had already started to wander before he got the shoes.

Being the youngest, Timothy was given his own way too much. He learned bad habits. Now and then he stayed away from school. Often he was late for dinner. His mother kept warning him, but it did no good. Finally, she decided to stand it no longer.

So one morning she had the leather shoes brightly blacked and the copper heels and toes shined. Then she saw to it that Timothy put on the shoes, and she sent him off to school.

"Now, Timothy, dear, you had better behave yourself," she warned him, though she had an idea he wouldn't. "And mind you go straight to school, or those shoes will pinch you hard, and you'll be sorry."

Timothy's face showed that he did not believe a word of the warning. The shoes felt good. He couldn't imagine how the shoes could pinch him later if they didn't pinch him already. He was off like the wind and did not give another thought to his mother's warning.

All winter the weather had been so cold that Timothy had not wanted to wander about on the way to school. But now on the day he first wore the fairy shoes, spring and warm weather had suddenly come.

The air was warm and sweet. The countryside was bright with sunshine and flowers. Down in the marsh the yellow cowslips were shining like gold. Birds were making music all about him.

The weather was just what it should be in the springtime. Timothy's feet did not hurry along the path.

Once or twice he stopped to pick some flowers, and each time the fairy shoes felt a little tight. They didn't really pinch, but he went on toward school, following a butterfly that seemed to be going the same way.

But when the butterfly flew off, and Timothy looked down from the path and saw the golden cowslips in the marsh, he forgot all about school.

Even though the bank between the path and the marsh looked long and steep, Timothy thought climbing down would be fun. He threw away the flowers he had picked. He wanted the shining cowslips with their golden cups and dark green leaves.

Timothy threw his books on the grass and started to climb down the steep bank beside the path. When he turned toward the cowslips, the shoes began to pinch hard.

Timothy did not give up easily. He insisted on going toward the marsh, though the shoes pinched so hard he thought they were going to pull his feet right off.

Finally he got himself, shoes and all, down the steep bank to the edge of the marsh. But there were no cowslips at the edge of the marsh. Most of them were deep in the marsh, far beyond his reach.

So Timothy wandered out into the muddy marsh. The shoes pulled at his feet and pinched him hard at every step.

At last he was in the middle of a bunch of cowslips that were quite near the edge of the marsh. The shoes were pinching harder than ever. No wonder! They were so deep in the mud that muddy water was running over the tops. Still Timothy went on.

Suddenly the pinching stopped. His feet felt comfortable. The sticky mud had pulled the shoes off his feet. In great delight, he wandered among the cowslips.

Timothy wondered why his brothers had not thrown the uncomfortable shoes into the marsh. Well, they were in the marsh now. Never again could they pinch his feet and insist on his going where he didn't want to go. Timothy was delighted.

But at last he got tired of wandering in the muddy marsh. He had gathered more cowslips than he could carry. He realized that he was late for school. So he hurried toward the edge of the marsh.

On the way he tripped on a pointed stick and hurt his foot. As he climbed up the steep bank, he had to drop most of the cowslips. Finally he reached the path. He was tired, muddy, and very uncomfortable.

He cleaned the mud off himself as best he could, took off his muddy stockings, and started on to school. He felt uncomfortable about leaving the shoes in the marsh, but he decided to go on without them.

Though Timothy had many bad habits and didn't always behave himself as he should, he never told anything that wasn't true.

He made up his mind to tell the teacher why he was late. He was still trying to think what to say when he found himself in school.

Timothy did not notice the teacher's cross look or see the smiles that passed among the children as he took his seat. His eyes were fixed upon the schoolroom floor. What he saw did not delight him.

There, under his own desk, stood the little leather shoes with the copper heels and toes. The shoes were covered with mud, and in each one was a big golden cowslip.

"You've been in the marsh, Timothy," the teacher said. "Put on your shoes and stockings!"

Timothy did as he was told, and all the rest of that day he behaved very well indeed, even when the boys teased him. After school was out, though, he had to sit at his desk for a while because he had been late.

When at last the teacher told him that he might go, he let his shoes take him straight home.

When Timothy's mother learned that he had been in the marsh, she decided that he must go to a boys' school, where someone would be able to make him behave. So she sent him to live with a man named Dr. White, who kept a school for boys of Timothy's age.

Timothy's mother insisted that he take with him the gift she had received from the fairy godmother.

Timothy liked the school. He liked being among the boys, even though they teased him about his shoes, and he liked Dr. White. Except for one thing he liked his teacher, who was called a master. The master insisted on making problems and examples about Timothy's shoes.

He would begin an example in this way: "If Timothy's shoes cost a dollar and a half without copper heels and toes, how much —?"

When the master was teaching the boys to speak correctly, he would ask, "Which is correct? Timothy's shoes are under his desk, or Timothy's shoes is under his desk?"

As you can see, Timothy's shoes received more attention than he liked.

Things went on that way until cherries began to get ripe. Then the shoes received less attention. Every day the boys would bring cherries and hide them in their desks. When the master found them, he took them. He made examples about cherries.

One day the master noticed that Timothy was half asleep in class and not paying attention to the examples. "Timothy!" he called. "Two hundred ten cherries added to one hundred six cherries will make —"

"A very big pie!" shouted Timothy.

Of course a pie was not the answer to the example, and Timothy was sent to the bottom of the class. Then, as always happened, the leather shoes pinched until he took them off. Then they pattered back to their place under his desk.

As long as Timothy was at the bottom of the class, he had to walk around in his stocking feet. The shoes insisted on staying under his desk until he got so ashamed of himself that he worked his way up to the head of the class.

If Timothy had learned to pay attention to the warnings that the magic shoes gave, he would have been much happier. Even though they made him feel ashamed of himself sometimes, they always warned him of danger and worked to bring him happiness.

He won races and games because the shoes helped him run faster and jump higher and farther than other boys could.

By paying attention to the shoes, Timothy could have kept out of trouble. Certainly he would never have had to stand in his stocking feet at the bottom of the class.

But Timothy imagined that he could be very happy if it were not for the shoes.

"I don't want to wander far or go the wrong way," he said many times. "I just want to go my own way, that's all."

Day and night he tried to think of a way to lose the magic shoes forever.

The Shoes Go to a Dance

When Timothy went home for vacation, his mother thought that he was behaving much better. He had at least learned what good habits were, and it seemed to her that he was losing some of his bad habits.

About a week after he arrived at home, a lady who lived in town asked him to a children's party and dance. Timothy was delighted, and so was his mother.

When the day came, she said, "I think I can trust you to go by yourself now, Timothy, especially in those magic shoes.

"You may go, but I insist on one thing. You must start home just as soon as the clock begins to strike ten. Now remember!

"If you come straight home, your feet will be comfortable. If you don't, I warn you that the shoes will pinch hard."

But Timothy didn't pay much attention to his mother's warning.

"If she trusts me to go by myself, she can trust me to come home at the right time," Timothy said to himself. "When the clock strikes ten, I won't need shoes to pinch my feet and make me uncomfortable.

"Besides, it is really too much to expect me to dance in leather shoes with copper toes and heels. I'll borrow a better pair."

So he borrowed a pair of shiny black leather shoes from the next older brother. The borrowed shoes were so big that he had to put paper into the toe of each shoe.

He went out by a little path behind the house so he wouldn't pass his mother's window. He was afraid she might see the borrowed shoes he wore and be cross.

The path came out on a narrow and poorly lighted street. Timothy could see queer-looking people walking among the shadows there. He felt uneasy.

For a few seconds he stopped. Then he started down the street, walking fast.

Suddenly he heard footsteps right behind him. He walked faster. Still the footsteps followed him. Then he began to run, but the footsteps stayed at his heels.

Timothy tried to run faster, but he couldn't. The borrowed shoes were so big that it was hard for him to run at all. He was afraid to stop and turn around, so he ran on as best he could.

The footsteps followed him down the narrow street, into Main Street, down Main Street, and up to the door of the house where the party was.

Timothy knocked at the door and then turned to see who had been chasing him. Nobody was behind him, but his little leather shoes stood beside him on the steps.

"Your shoes, sir?" asked the polite footman who opened the door. He carried the shoes inside. Timothy put them on and left the borrowed shoes with the footman.

"If I don't wear my own shoes," he said to himself, "they'll be coming upstairs, and people will laugh at me."

Timothy had no reason to be sorry about the change. Other people were not nearly so interested in his clothes as he was himself, and the shoes danced so well that every girl at the party wanted Timothy to be her partner.

He went down twice to supper and ate as much spice cake as possible. Everyone was just about to dance a square dance when the clock on Main Street began to strike ten. The shoes began to feel tight.

Timothy knew he ought to go, but a pretty little girl was teasing him to be her partner, and square dancing was the kind he liked best. He decided he would stay just until that one dance was over. He took the little girl for his partner, and the dance began.

But when he began to dance, the shoes
pinched and pulled and refused to behave.
Once, when he was supposed to dance down
the middle of the room with his partner, the
shoes insisted on turning him around and
then carried him off toward the door.

Of course his partner didn't like that.
Timothy knew he must either make the shoes
behave better or stop dancing. He knew no
reason why he shouldn't take off the
uncomfortable shoes for a few minutes. So
he did and tried to dance in his stocking feet.

But when the shoes were off, Timothy
discovered that something else was wrong
with his dancing. It hardly seemed possible,
but he couldn't remember what to do.

231

He turned his partner around when he should have bowed, and he bowed when he should have taken his partner's hand. When he was leading a long line of boys, he took them all in the wrong direction.

The boys scolded, and the girls said he had eaten too much spice cake.

In a few minutes Timothy was so ashamed that he left the dancers and went downstairs. He got the borrowed shoes from the footman, put them on, and started home. He ran down Main Street to make up for lost time.

As he turned out of Main Street into the dark, narrow street, he discovered that the leather shoes were ahead of him, leading the way home. The copper heels and toes flashed as they went under a street lamp.

When he reached his own door, the little shoes were waiting for him on the doorstep.

A Job Well Done

During the days Timothy was at home, the magic shoes started him on some good habits. He seemed to be learning to behave.

When he went back to school, winter weather had come. Snow lay on the fields, and ice covered the lakes. The magic shoes helped him go far and fast on the snow and ice and always in the right direction.

Timothy was no longer ashamed to wear them. Whenever he wore them now, he was really glad he had not lost them.

The boys played follow the leader in the snow and made big snowmen. They threw snowballs and buried things deep in the snow for Dr. White's big dog, Nardy, to find.

"If we ever get lost in the snow, Nardy should be able to find us," said Timothy's best friend, Roger, one day.

One Saturday afternoon the master took Timothy and Roger for a long walk. They couldn't find Nardy, so they went without him. They stopped to visit a friendly farmer and were late starting back.

A fine snow was beginning to fall. But though it was fine, it soon covered the road and the tops of the stone walls.

The master thought it wise to get home as quickly as possible, so he decided to take a path across the fields instead of following the road.

He and the boys climbed a wall and trudged along the path through the snow. But in a short time the snow was falling so fast and thick that no one could see more than a few yards ahead. Soon the path was completely buried under the fallen snow.

The soft snow went down their necks and into their eyes and ears. Their hands and feet became colder and colder until they lost all feeling.

Timothy was almost ready to cry. He was cold, and his shoes were pinching hard.

"Your shoes are uncomfortable because we're not on the road," said the master. "But this short cut will save time. In five minutes we shall strike the stone wall and the road again. Then the shoes won't hurt any more. Try to bear the pinching a few minutes longer."

But Timothy found the pinching so hard to bear that the master took him on his back and held his feet in his hands. Roger took off the shoes and carried them.

Five minutes passed, but they did not strike either the road or the wall. Five minutes more went by. Timothy lay heavy on the master's back, for he was asleep, but the master's heart was heavier still.

The storm got worse and worse. Now the path was buried so deep under the thick snow that no sign of it could be seen.

"Roger, we've lost our way," said the master. "Put down Timothy's shoes. We'll try to follow them."

The shoes tripped ahead lightly over the top of the snow, while the master and Roger trudged slowly through it. In a few seconds the shoes had disappeared completely in the thick snowfall.

Roger began to cry. "I'm too tired to go any farther," he said. "Leave me here."

Of course the master could not bear to do that. He woke Timothy and insisted that he put on Roger's overshoes and walk. He took Roger on his back.

"Hold onto the edge of my coat, Timothy," said the master. "I'll make a path for you."

Timothy took hold of the master's coat, and the two trudged on through the storm. The master hoped they were going in the same direction the shoes had gone.

It was dark now and much colder.

"How are you getting on, Timothy?" the master asked after a while.

He got no answer, but he thought he felt a pull on his coat.

"Hold tight to my coat and don't be afraid!" he said as cheerfully as possible.

There was no sound from Timothy.

After a few minutes more, the master called out, "Don't lose heart, boy!"

When no sound came from Timothy, the master looked back. *Timothy was not there!* He had disappeared in the storm.

"What shall I do?" thought the unhappy man. "I must either go on and try to save Roger's life or turn back after Timothy and perhaps lose all our lives."

He turned around as he spoke. The wild wind drove the snow into his face. The storm was getting much worse. Yet the master chose to go back.

He found Timothy almost buried in the snow, but by then he was so tired that he lay down beside Timothy to rest a while.

In the afternoon when Dr. White first noticed that snow was falling, he said, "The weatherman is dropping a little sugar on our friends." The boys laughed, for this was one of Dr. White's winter jokes.

But when it began to get dark and the storm became worse, the boys noticed that Dr. White looked uneasy. "I hope they will come home soon," he said.

Soon it was completely dark. Outside, the snow was falling thick and fast. Dr. White tried not to let the boys know that he was worried.

"It's possible that our friends have stopped at a farm," he said. A minute or so later he added, "Of course they are staying at a farm. A wise thing to do in this kind of weather."

He sat down with his newspaper and a cup of coffee. But he did not enjoy either one. Every few minutes he threw aside his paper, opened the door, and looked out.

He could see nothing but the thick snow falling and hear nothing but the wind.

But when he opened the door for the fifth time, Timothy's shoes ran in. They were filled with snow.

Right away the doctor sent to the town for help. He put a pail of water on the stove so there would be hot water for lemonade to warm up the lost travelers should they be found. Then he put on his heavy leggings and his overcoat and wool cap, took a light, and went out into the yard.

There lay the dog Nardy with his big nose at the door of his doghouse, smelling the storm. When he saw the light and Dr. White, his large eyes became bright.

In a few minutes the men from the town arrived. Nardy was so eager to be off that he almost broke his rope.

The doctor untied the rope and tied Timothy's shoes around Nardy's neck.

"Perhaps they will help to lead their wearer in the right direction," he said.

Snow was falling so thick and fast now that Nardy often disappeared completely ahead of the men.

"If some dogs weren't smarter than people," said a man, "we'd all lose our way."

Just then the sound of Nardy's deep voice came back through the storm.

"He has found something!" cried a man.

"He must have discovered our friends," said Dr. White, and all trudged on eagerly in the direction Nardy had gone.

Dr. White was right. Nardy had found Timothy, Roger, and the master. They were buried in the snow, but they were still alive. The magic shoes, Nardy, and the men had saved their lives.

From that time on, Timothy was delighted to wear the magic shoes. Never again was he ashamed of the wonderful gift. He would as soon have been ashamed of those other friends, the master and Nardy.

But too often we do not realize how wonderful our best friends are until they are about to be taken from us. So it was with Timothy. He was outgrowing his shoes.

Timothy was at home when the day came on which his feet would no longer go into the little shoes. He shined them, as he had often done before, and put them away in a cupboard in his mother's room. He was very sad as he set them on the shelf and closed the cupboard door.

Timothy's mother felt very sad, too. She could not sleep that night. She kept thinking of the shoes in the cupboard and of how thankful she was for the help the godmother's gift had been.

The sun was just coming up when she woke and heard a sound that she had often heard before — the sound of a boy jumping from a high place to the floor.

"Oh, dear, that boy will hurt himself!" she cried from habit.

As she spoke, she noticed that the cupboard door was open. Then she saw the magic shoes coming toward her bed. They stopped for a minute by the bed as if to say good-by, and then the bedroom door opened to let them pass. Down the stairs they ran lightly, pitter-patter, pitter-patter.

"The front door is locked," thought the mother. "They can't leave yet."

But just then she heard the front door slowly open. She jumped out of bed, threw open the window, and leaned out.

In front of the house was a little garden with a gate leading to the road. Beyond the road was a hill with a path going over it.

The little shoes pitter-pattered through the garden. The gate opened for them and closed behind them. Then they crossed the road and went up the path on the hill.

The mother watched while they became smaller and smaller. At last they turned a corner and disappeared. When the sun looked over the hill, Timothy's shoes were gone.

Say the words **strange, street,** and **stripe** slowly and listen to the sound that the three letters **str** stand for.

Say **strong, string, stretch, straight,** and listen for the sound that **str** stands for.

Instead of **cr** in **cream,** put in the letters **str.** Make the word **stream.**

Which of these animals live in streams? cats   crocodiles   horses   fish   dogs

Instead of **s** in **say** and **saw,** put in **str.** Make **stray** and **straw.**

Is a stray dog one that stays at home, or is it one that has gone away from home?

Would a pile of wood make a worse bed for a cow than a pile of straw?

Instead of **l** in **like** and **luck,** put in **str.** Make **strike** and **struck.**

When a man drives a nail into a board, does he stretch it, strike it, or string it?

A car was struck by a truck. Did the car strike the truck, or did the truck strike the car?

Read each sentence carefully. If it tells
you to do something, do it as well as you can.
If it asks a question, decide how to answer it
correctly.

Say the words **three, throw,** and **threw**
slowly and listen to hear the sound that the
letters **thr** stand for.

Take **c** away from **coat.** Put in **thr** to
make the word **throat.**

In what part of your body is your throat?

Which of these things can you do without
using your throat?

cry   paint   laugh   stretch   smile

Take **h** away from **head.** Put in **thr** to
make the word **thread.**

What does your mother use thread for?

Which of these things is the strongest?

string   wire   thread   rope

If you went to a store to buy some thread,
which of these things should you ask for?

a stool of thread   a school of thread

a stall of thread   a spool of thread

The Dinner Bell

"Tony!"

Tony Minelli heard his mother's call, but he lay still and kept his eyes closed. He wished that he could close his ears, too, and not be bothered.

Tony had come back from working in the vegetable garden where it was hot, and he had just stretched out on the grass under a tree. He was very comfortable there.

"Tony Minelli!" His mother's voice was kind but too clear to go unnoticed.

"Yes, Mother!" he answered as he got up and walked toward the kitchen door.

"Ring the dinner bell, please," she said. "Dinner will be ready in a few minutes."

The dinner bell hung in a wooden frame above the kitchen. The frame was so old that it shook as the bell rang. The wood was cracked and needed paint. The bell rope hung down just outside the kitchen wall.

When Mr. Minelli and Tony's brother Tom were at work in the fields, it was Tony's job to ring the bell twice a day. He rang it at noon to call them to dinner, and he rang it at night to call them to supper.

Tony had started ringing the bell when he was just a small boy. It was fun then, but now it was a bother. As he pulled on the rope, he kept trying to plan some way to get out of the job.

As Tony continued to pull and plan, King came trotting around the corner of the house. King was a very smart dog that was curious about everything, especially if it was moving. The end of the bell rope caught the dog's attention at once.

Tony noticed King's interest. "Look, King!" he said, as he stopped ringing the bell and held the rope so that the end hung just above King's nose. "You learn to ring this old bell, and I won't have to bother with it."

Tony shook the rope, and King jumped up and caught it between his teeth. Then off he ran as far as the rope would let him go.

Ding! went the bell. Tony laughed and called King to him. Dong! went the bell as King came back. Tony was delighted. King wagged his tail to show his happiness.

"You really can ring the old bell," Tony exclaimed. "Good dog! Smart dog!"

He reached down and scratched King behind his ears. King liked that and continued to ring the bell in his own dog way. It sounded strange.

Sometimes ding and dong were close together, but often they were far apart. That was when King held the rope tight too long. King rang the bell so loud that the old frame on the roof shook.

Mr. Minelli and Tom were at work when Tony began to ring the bell. They stopped work. As they started for the house, the bell began to ring in a strange way.

"That bell sounds queer," said Mr. Minelli.

"I wonder what's the matter," said Tom.

They soon found out when they reached the yard. There was King, with the bell rope between his teeth.

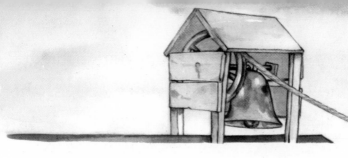

"I see that we have a new bell ringer this noon," said Mr. Minelli. "I trust that he won't be so slow as the old one was about calling us to meals."

Tony laughed. He was used to being teased about how slow he was.

Mrs. Minelli and Jane came out to see what all the noise was about. Jane was delighted as King continued to ring the bell. Her mother was not so well pleased. Dinner had been waiting several minutes.

"So, King, you are the noise-maker!" exclaimed Mrs. Minelli. "I thought that something was wrong. Stop that noise!"

King was so surprised that he dropped the rope from between his teeth and hung his head. Jane felt sorry for him. She bent down to scratch him behind the ears. "Smart King!" she said. "Smart dog!"

King felt better right away.

While Mr. and Mrs. Minelli, Tony, Tom, and Jane were eating their noon meal, the bell on the roof began to ring again. Ding, dong! Ding, dong! Tony rushed out into the yard.

There was King holding the bell rope between his teeth and looking much pleased with himself.

"King! Drop that rope!" ordered Tony.

King let go of the rope, hung his head, and ran off with his tail between his legs as Tony chased him out of the yard.

When Tony went back to the dinner table, his father said, "It was clever of King to learn to ring the bell. But you must teach him to ring it only when you order him to. It may have been a mistake to teach him to ring it."

"I'll try to make him behave," said Tony.

That was a harder job than Tony expected it to be. Time after time King got the bell rope between his teeth, but Tony was able to stop him before he rang the bell.

Late that afternoon Tony had to go to the barn for chicken feed. He didn't bother to take King along. The job took only a minute or two.

While Tony was getting the chicken feed, he heard the dinner bell give one little ding. He looked around for King, but the dog was not in sight.

Tony knew it was much too early to call Tom and his father home. He rushed to the house to stop King, but he was too late. The bell was ringing loud and clear now.

"King!" Tony scolded. "Stop it! You aren't supposed to ring that bell unless I order you to. You are a bad dog."

King dropped the rope from between his teeth, hung his head, and put his tail between his legs. He didn't like to be scolded. He looked very sad.

Tony couldn't stay angry. He gave King a quick pat. "I know you don't mean to be bad," he said. "It was my mistake to teach you to ring that bell."

Tony knew that when his father and Tom heard the bell, they would think either that it was time for supper or that something was wrong. Anyhow, they would surely come home unless he told them not to.

"I'd better go to meet them and tell them what happened," thought Tony. He started walking across the hayfield.

As soon as Tom and his father came in sight, Tony ran to meet them and told them just what had happened.

"I'm not going to scold you, Tony," Mr. Minelli said. "We all make mistakes. But you must keep King from ringing that bell."

"King won't bother you after this," said Tony. "I promise to make him behave."

Keep the Bell!

That evening, Mr. Minelli stood in the yard, looking thoughtfully at the bell that hung in the old frame on the kitchen roof.

"The crack in the old frame is getting worse," said Mr. Minelli. "I've been meaning to get some boards and nails and fix it, but maybe we should get rid of the old bell."

He walked over and took hold of the rope. "Maybe I could put this too high up on the wall for King to reach it," he continued. "But if I did, Tony couldn't reach it either. I guess the best thing is to get rid of the old bell. Then King can't ring it and Tony won't have to bother about it."

Even though Tony thought ringing the bell was a bother, he really liked to hear its deep and clear ding, dong.

"Don't get rid of it, Dad," he said. "I'm sure King won't ring it again unless I order him to."

"I'd miss that old bell," said Mrs. Minelli. "I like to feel that I can call you home at any hour I need to."

"I've listened for it ever since I was a little boy," said Tom. "I'd miss it, too, if you got rid of it."

Then little Jane spoke up. "I like the bell. Let King ring it now."

Everyone laughed at that, and Mr. Minelli said, "Well, we'll leave the bell up for a little while. But if King rings it again when he shouldn't, I'll surely get rid of it."

During the rest of that week Tony kept a close watch on King. On Sunday King seemed especially worried when Tony kept him from ringing the bell at all. He couldn't understand the reason for that.

On Monday, Tuesday, and Wednesday King behaved very well indeed. He showed that he had learned not to ring the bell unless Tony ordered him to.

On Thursday after dinner, Mrs. Minelli said, "Tony, I wish that you would look after the house for an hour or two. Mrs. White down on Main Street hasn't been well lately. Jane and I are going to see her."

Shortly after Tom and Mr. Minelli had returned to the fields, Tony's mother and little Jane went off down the road. Tony and King were left alone at the farmhouse.

Tony had worked in the vegetable garden all morning. He was tired. He stretched out on the grass in the shadow of a tree and soon fell sound asleep.

He had been asleep almost an hour when King woke him up. He was running around wildly and barking.

Tony sat up on the grass, his eyes still half shut. What was that noise he heard? Was there a queer smell in the air? Maybe he just imagined those things. He lay down again. Then King came rushing back from the house, barking louder than ever.

"King never barks unless something is wrong," thought Tony. "I wonder what's the matter."

King rushed toward the kitchen, barking excitedly. Tony followed after him and soon discovered what was wrong. Smoke was beginning to pour out through the kitchen doorway and windows.

"The kitchen is on fire!" Tony shouted. Then he realized that no one else was at home. He would have to put out the fire alone.

Ring the Bell!

Tony ran to the kitchen door and looked in. Through the thick smoke he noticed little flames coming out of the wall behind the stove. He picked up a pail of water, rushed into the smoke, and threw the water at the flames.

But the water didn't go quite high enough. The flames were spreading. Soon they would burn their way to the roof. Tony rushed back outside and stopped to clear the smoke out of his eyes. He realized there was no time to lose.

The flames were spreading fast, and the smoke was getting thicker. He knew that it would take more water than he could pour on the flames to put them out. Unless he got help from somewhere, the farmhouse would burn down. If only he had a fire alarm!

"Fire! Fire!" he shouted. King barked and barked. But there was no one near to hear. And the flames had spread to the roof.

Suddenly Tony thought of a way to spread the alarm. He called King and ran to the bell rope. "Ring the bell, King! Ring the bell!" he ordered. Then he rushed back and threw more water on the flames.

Down in the field Mr. Minelli thought that he heard the dinner bell. He stopped his tractor and listened. "That sounds like our dinner bell!" he exclaimed.

"It certainly does," said Tom, "but there's no reason to ring it at this hour of the day. I suppose that silly dog is ringing it again."

"I suppose so," said Mr. Minelli. "Well, we can't be bothered this time. Tony made a big mistake when he helped King learn that trick."

The bell continued to ring. Ding, dong! Ding, dong! Ding, dong! Ding, dong! Mr. Minelli began to be alarmed.

"That bell is ringing much longer than usual," he said. "It seems as though Tony could have stopped King by now. I wonder if something is wrong."

"Mother and Jane went to visit Mrs. White," said Tom. "Tony is all alone. Perhaps he's in trouble or asleep. If everything's all right, I'm certain he wouldn't let King ring the bell so long in the middle of the afternoon."

"I think we'd better get up to the house right away," said Mr. Minelli. "Come on!"

He and Tom ran toward the house. All the time the bell continued to ring. Ding, dong! Ding, dong! Ding, dong!

Tony's mother heard the dinner bell, too. "Dear me! That sounds like our dinner bell!" she exclaimed to Mrs. White. "I wonder if King is ringing it again."

The bell rang on and on. Ding, dong! Ding, dong! Ding, dong!

Mrs. Minelli became alarmed when the ringing continued. "Something must be the matter," she said. "I think Jane and I had better go home right away."

As she and Jane hurried toward the house, they saw neighbors running from all directions. Several men carried pails.

"When a dinner bell rings like that, it is usually sounding an alarm for some kind of trouble," said one man as he passed Jane and her mother. "And trouble around here is usually a fire."

When the neighbors and the family came in sight of the house, they could see smoke pouring out of it, and flames spreading over the roof.

261

When they arrived, they lost no time getting to work. Some of the men pulled up pails of water from the well. Others stood in line between the well and the house and passed the pails along the line. The men at the end of the line threw the water on the flames.

The men worked fast. In less than half an hour the fire was completely out. Not until then had anyone noticed that King was still ringing the bell. Even when Tony ordered him to stop, he held the rope between his teeth for some time.

"It's a good thing Tony was here to start pouring water on the flames," Mr. Minelli said. "He kept the fire from spreading and saved our nice old house."

"I didn't do it alone," said Tony. "King discovered the fire and barked and barked to let me know about it. Then he rang the alarm. If he hadn't helped, the house would have burned down."

"Good dog!" said Jane, patting King.

Mother said, "I'm glad we didn't get rid of the old bell. If we had, King couldn't have sounded the alarm, and none of us would have known that there was a fire until it was too late. The fire could have been much, much worse."

"I wouldn't think of getting rid of that old bell now," said Mr. Minelli. "Tom and I will take down the bell and the old frame and fix the roof. Then we'll build a completely new frame and put the old bell back in it."

"And we'll let Tony and King continue to be the bell ringers," said Mrs. Minelli.

"Smart King!" said Jane.

Umbrellas

On rainy days you can see umbrellas of many different sizes and colors bobbing along the street as people walk under them to keep out of the rain.

The first umbrellas, however, were not used to keep off rain. They were used in hot countries to keep off the sun. People enjoyed walking in the little shadows that the umbrellas made. Long ago the meaning of the word umbrella was "little shadow."

For many years umbrellas were used only by very rich people. Kings and other important people had servants who held umbrellas over them to keep off the hot sun. Even today in some countries only important people own umbrellas.

The next time you carry an umbrella, remember that many years ago you would have had to be very important to own one.

The Stonecutter

Once upon a time, there was a stonecutter named Hofus. He used to go every day to a rock mountain to cut out blocks of stone for the builders of fine houses.

The stonecutter lived near the mountain in a little wooden house. His house was small, his clothes were ragged, and he sometimes went hungry. But he worked hard, and he was usually happy.

One day Hofus took a few blocks of stone and went to do some work at the house of a rich man who lived in the city.

Hofus noticed that the rich man had power over many servants and that his house was filled with beautiful furniture. When Hofus went back to his work of cutting blocks of stone on the mountain, he could think of nothing else but the powerful, rich man.

As he worked hard cutting the blocks of stone from the steep sides of the mountain, Hofus began to wish that he, too, might have power over many servants and a house filled with beautiful furniture. Very softly he said to himself,

"Ah me! Ah me!
If Hofus only were rich as he!"

To his surprise, a voice from inside the mountain answered,

"You have your wish!"

When Hofus returned home that evening, his little house had disappeared. In its place stood a great palace. The palace was filled with beautiful furniture.

Hofus was so rich that he didn't need to work any more. He had power over many servants. They did all that needed to be done, and there was nothing left for him to do.

At first he was delighted not to have to cut blocks of stone all day long. But he was not used to doing nothing, and soon the time began to pass very slowly.

One day, as he walked near his palace, an open coach came down the street. In it sat a prince wearing a purple robe. Behind him stood his servants, dressed in blue and silver. One servant held a golden umbrella over the prince's head.

Hofus took off his hat and bowed to the prince. Then he began to wonder why the prince should have more power than he had. He began to feel very unhappy and said,

"Ah me! Ah me!
If Hofus only a prince might be!"

And again the same voice that he had heard on the mountain spoke. It said,

"Be now a prince!"

Immediately Hofus became a rich and powerful prince. He rode in a golden coach, and a servant held a golden umbrella over his head. Everyone took off his hat and bowed when the prince's coach went by.

His country was a large one, and his power was very great. For a short time he was happy. He liked being a prince. It delighted him to be called "your Majesty," or "his Majesty." He liked especially being so rich and powerful.

But one day, as his Majesty was walking among the flowers in the palace garden, he noticed that the earth was very dry. The flowers were no longer fresh and bright, and the grass was dry and brown.

When he rode out in his coach, he discovered that the hot sun burned him, even through the golden umbrella.

"What good are my power and my riches?" he thought. "The sun is mightier than I." And he said to himself,

"Ah me! Ah me!
If Hofus only the sun might be!"

268

And the voice answered,
"Be now the sun!"

Immediately he became the great sun. High above the earth he stood, with greater power and majesty than any prince. He burned the grass and the flowers and dried up the rivers. Rich people and poor people alike were burned brown by him. He was delighted with his power.

One day, however, a thick cloud appeared and stretched itself between him and the dry earth. Hofus quickly discovered that he no longer had the power to dry up the rivers and the grass and the flowers.

He insisted that the cloud go away and became very angry when the cloud continued to stay between him and the earth. He cried,
"Ah me! Ah me!
If Hofus only a cloud might be!"
And the voice answered,
"Be now a cloud!"

Immediately Hofus became a thick cloud, a rain cloud between the hot sun and the dry earth.

Then, day after day, the cloud poured rain on the earth. Rivers ran over their banks and covered the fields with water. Whole towns were washed away. Only the great rocks on the mountainside stood unmoved as the rain poured down.

The cloud looked at them in wonder and said,

"Ah me! Ah me!

If Hofus only a rock might be!"

And the voice answered,

"Be now a rock!"

Immediately he became a rock. Proudly he stood. The sun could not burn him. The rain could not move him.

"Now, at last," he said to himself, "no one is mightier than I!"

But one day a noise woke him up. Tap! Tap! Tap! It was down at his feet. He looked, and there was a stonecutter cutting into the rock! Another tap, and the great rock shook. Then a block of the stone broke away.

"That man is mightier than I!" cried Hofus, and he said sadly,

"Ah me! Ah me!
If Hofus only the man might be!"

And, for the last time, the voice answered,

"Be now the man!"

Immediately Hofus was himself again — a poor stonecutter who worked all day cutting blocks of stone out of the steep mountainside and went home at night to his little wooden house. But he was happy, and never again did he wish to be other than Hofus, the stonecutter.

Brother Fox

and the Barbecues

Brother Rabbit has told many stories about Brother Fox, Brother Wolf, Brother Bear, and himself. These stories are always interesting because when Brother Fox and the other animals get together, funny things happen.

In the story that comes next, Brother Bear and Brother Wolf each have a barbecue. A barbecue is a big outdoor party. Everyone likes to go to a barbecue because there are sure to be all kinds of good things to eat. Everyone has a good time.

At a barbecue the food is cooked outdoors over open fires, as the picture above shows. The smell of good things cooking fills the air.

Now let Brother Rabbit tell you about Brother Fox and the two barbecues.

Once upon a time, when Brother Fox and I were getting along very well, we were asked to come to a barbecue that Brother Wolf was going to give on the following Wednesday. The next day we were asked to come to a barbecue that Brother Bear was going to give on the same Wednesday.

I chose at once to go to Brother Bear's barbecue, because I knew he would have roast corn with plenty of butter and salt, and if there's any one thing on earth that tastes better than another, it's roast corn with lots of butter and salt.

I asked Brother Fox whether he was going to Brother Bear's barbecue or to Brother Wolf's. He said he hadn't been able to make up his mind. First he thought he'd go to one place, and then he thought he'd go to the other.

I went about my work as usual. Cold weather was coming on, and I wanted to get my vegetables in before winter. But I noticed that Brother Fox was mighty upset in his mind. Something was troubling him. He didn't do a bit of work.

He'd sit down, and then he'd get up. He'd stand still and look up at the treetops. Then he'd walk back and forth with his hands behind him and look down at the ground.

I said to him, "I hope you're not sick, Brother Fox."

Said he, "Oh, no, Brother Rabbit. I don't feel a bit sick. I never felt better in my life."

Then I said, "I hope you'll be coming along with me to Brother Bear's barbecue tomorrow. He'll be having roast corn, and it'll taste mighty good. Or are you going to Brother Wolf's barbecue?"

Said he, "I can't tell, Brother Rabbit. I can't tell. I haven't made up my mind. I may go to the one, or I may go to the other, but which it will be, I can't tell you to save my life."

The next day was Wednesday. I was up bright and early. I took time to dig my potatoes and spread them out to dry in the sun before I went to the barbecue. The clock was striking ten when I started out for Brother Bear's house.

Brother Wolf lived near the river, and Brother Bear lived right by the river, a mile or two beyond Brother Wolf's. About three miles beyond my house, the big road forks. One fork leads to Brother Wolf's house, and the other fork leads to Brother Bear's house.

Well, when I came within sight of the forks in the road, who should be there but old Brother Fox! I stopped before he saw me and watched him. He didn't appear to be sick, but he was acting mighty queerly.

275

He was just walking back and forth, back and forth. He'd go a little way down the road toward Brother Bear's and stop there and wait a bit. Then he'd come back to the forks and go a little way down the road toward Brother Wolf's and stop there and wait a bit.

After a while, I went up to him to pass the time of day and be on my way. I told him that if he was planning on going to Brother Bear's barbecue, I'd be glad to have his company.

But he said that he wouldn't keep me waiting. He had just come down to the forks in the road to see if that would help him make up his mind.

I told him I was mighty sorry to miss his company and his talk. Then I tipped my hat and went on down the road toward Brother Bear's house.

Well, when I smelled the roast meat at that barbecue, I was really glad I had come — really glad. Brother Bear had lamb and goat, cooked to a turn, and roast pig that made my mouth water. The roast corn tasted so good that I can hardly stand telling about it.

I'll not tell you any more about that dinner except that I'd like to have one like it every Wednesday in the year. If I happened to be too sick to eat it, I could sit up and look at it. Anyhow, we all had enough to eat and then some.

After we had finished with the barbecue
and were sitting on Brother Bear's front
porch, I said that I thought I'd go by Brother
Wolf's house as I went on home. Even
though it was a right smart step out of the
way, I wanted to see how the land lay.

Said Brother Bear, "If you'll wait until
my company leaves, I don't mind trotting
over to Brother Wolf's with you. The walk
will do me good."

So, about two hours before sundown, we
set out by ourselves for Brother Wolf's
house. Brother Bear knew a short cut across
the marsh, and it didn't take us more than
half an hour to get there.

Brother Wolf was just telling his company
good-by. When they had all gone, he said to
us, "Come in for a taste of my roast lamb.
And I think there's a little roast pig left.
You can't leave without tasting that."

So we went in and tasted what food he had left, and believe me it was mighty tasty. After a while I said, "Brother Wolf, have you seen Brother Fox today?"

Brother Wolf said, "No, I haven't seen hide or hair of Brother Fox. I can't understand why he didn't come. He's always eager to go where there's fresh meat roasting. He must be sick."

I said, "I don't think he's sick. When I left Brother Fox at the forks in the road this morning, he was trying to make up his mind whether he'd eat at your house or at Brother Bear's."

"I'm mighty sorry," said Brother Wolf. "Whatever his reason, Brother Fox never missed a finer chance to pick a bone than he's had today. Please tell him so for me."

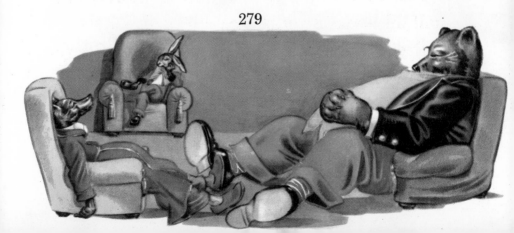

I said I would, and then I told Brother Wolf
and Brother Bear good-by and set out for
home. I came to the forks in the road just
before the sun went down.

You may not believe it, but when I got
there, Brother Fox was there, still going back
and forth, back and forth. He'd go down
one road and back and then down the other
road and back.

Said I, "I hope you had a good dinner at
Brother Wolf's today, Brother Fox."

Said he, "I've had no dinner."

Said I, "That's mighty funny. Brother
Bear had a wonderful barbecue. I thought
Brother Wolf was going to have one too."

Said Brother Fox, "Is dinner over? Is it
too late to go?"

Said I, "Why, Brother Fox, the sun's nearly down. By the time you get to Brother Bear's house, he'll be gone to bed, and by the time you get across the marsh to Brother Wolf's house, the roosters will be saying the sun is coming up."

"Well, well, well!" said Brother Fox. "I've been all day trying to make up my mind which road I'd take, and now it's too late."

And that was true. Poor Brother Fox had been at the forks of the road all day, trying to make up his mind which fork he'd take. And not a bit of dinner had he had.

Cloud Magic

The wind was playfully catching clouds,
And juggling them under his tent of blue,
And making parades of animal shapes
That never were seen in circus or zoo.

One cloud was a fish with a calf-like head,
And while we wondered what it would do,
It put on legs, sat down on its tail,
And turned itself into a kangaroo.

Tom saw a cloud that he called a giraffe.
Its head and its neck were surprisingly long.
But soon it got feathers, lost two of its legs,
And looked like an ostrich parading along.

One little cloud turned somersaults fast,
Over and over and upside down.
I didn't see what was inside, but I'm sure
That it was a bunch of juggling clowns.

Soon a long black cloud, like a crocodile,
Came up with its great mouth opened wide
And rushed at the sun. We shouted "Stop!"
But the sun had disappeared inside.

As the crocodile cloud moved quickly on,
It changed to a Chinese dragon instead,
With flaming eyes and, along its back,
An edge of fire from tail to head.

283

The story you will read next is somewhat different from the stories that you have been reading. It is printed as a play.

You will notice that the play has several different parts called scenes. When you are reading and you come to a different scene, you will find things happening in a different place.

In the first scene the people are in a farm kitchen. The second scene is on a road. The third scene is back in the farm kitchen. Each change of place brings a different scene.

When you take the part of a person in the play, try to say what that person said just the way you think he said it. If you act out the part of some person in the play, try to do just what you think that person did.

In the play you will often come to directions that are printed between marks like these ( ). Those directions tell you what to do or how to say something. Follow every one of such directions carefully.

Manwick

Goes to Town

MANWICK   KING

MANWICK'S MOTHER   PRINCESS

FIRST FOOTMAN   PEOPLE OF THE PALACE

SECOND FOOTMAN   DOGS

Scene 1

Time: A hot morning, long ago

Place: A farmhouse

(Manwick comes into the kitchen. His mother is holding a large jar.)

MOTHER: So you're back in the house again, Manwick. It's a long time to dinner. You won't make a good farmer unless you work harder. Do you feel sick?

285

MANWICK: I feel all right, Mother. But it's very hot, working in the cornfield. What's in that jar you're holding?

MOTHER: It's butter. I've just made it from our fresh, sweet cream. I wish I had somebody I could trust to go to town and sell it for me. I have so much work to do here in the kitchen that I don't want to take time to go myself.

MANWICK: I'll go to town for you, Mother. Let me sell the butter for you.

MOTHER: You, Manwick? You couldn't sell anything in town. You've never been away from this farm. You don't have any idea what a town is!

MANWICK: Please, Mother! You can tell me about the town. Then I'll be able to sell the butter for you.

MOTHER: Well, you're a young man now. It's time you took some work off my hands. All right, Manwick. You may take the butter to town for me.

You'll know the town when you come to it because it is so big. When you get to the town you won't have much trouble selling such good butter.

MANWICK: Thank you, Mother. I'll come back with a lot of money in my pockets. You'll be glad you sent me.

MOTHER: I hope so. Wash your hands and face and put on your good clothes before you start for town.

MANWICK: I'll be ready in a little while. I'll sell all the butter, and I'll bring home plenty of money. You'll see, Mother.

Scene 2

Time: About an hour later

Place: On the road that goes to town

(Manwick walks in from the side. He stops at a large rock.)

MANWICK: I've walked a long way from our farm. I must be in sight of the town now. Where can it be? Mother told me that the town is very big.

Oh, here is something very big! This must be the town. (He walks over to the big rock.) I'll talk politely to it, and ask if it wants to buy my butter.

Good morning, Friend Town. It's a very hot morning, isn't it? What did you say? You won't say anything at all? Maybe you think it's too hot to talk. That's right.

Would you like to buy some butter? It is very, very good butter. Mother made it from our sweet cream. Just taste a little bit of it. I'll put some on your head. I can't see where your mouth is.

(Manwick puts a little butter on the rock with one finger.)

Your head feels very hot when I touch you. The cold butter will make you feel better. I see that the little bit of butter is all gone. That means that you like it, I'm sure, and you want more. Is that right?

Very well. I'll put all the butter from my jar on you. Here it is. (Manwick puts the butter, little by little, on the rock until the jar is empty. He watches while the butter runs all over the hot rock.)

Now you have all my butter, Friend Town. Will you pay me for it, please? What's that? You have nothing to say? That means you have no money today. Well, you may pay me tomorrow. I'll come back tomorrow at this same time.

Be sure you have the money ready for me when I come. Good-by, Friend Town. (He walks off.)

289

Scene 3

Time: A short time later

Place: The kitchen of the farmhouse again

MOTHER: Well, Manwick, you are back very soon. Did you sell the butter, or at least some of it, in town?

MANWICK: Yes, Mother, all of it. Look! The jar is empty. (He holds out the empty jar.)

MOTHER: That's fine, my boy! How much money did you get for the butter? I hope it was enough to pay you for your trouble. Please let me have the money.

MANWICK: Well, he didn't have the money today. He'll pay me tomorrow.

MOTHER: He? Who is he?

MANWICK: The town. You wanted the town to buy the butter, didn't you?

MOTHER: But the money? Who will pay for the butter?

MANWICK: Why, the town, Mother.

MOTHER: The town will pay? That doesn't make any sense to me.

MANWICK: Just be patient until tomorrow, Mother. I'll get the money tomorrow, I promise.

MOTHER: Well, there's nothing I can do about it now. I should have known better than to trust you with such a job. It was a mistake to send you with the butter. Go out and work in the cornfield now.

MANWICK: You will get the money, Mother. Just be patient.

Scene 4

Time: The next day

Place: The place in the road where the big rock stands

(Manwick walks in and over to the rock.)

MANWICK: Good morning, Friend Town. I'm back again. I've come for the money for my butter, the butter you took from me. Give me my money, please.

What's that? You won't say anything? You won't give me my money? You should be ashamed of yourself. (Manwick is very angry.)

Give me my money! You won't? I'll show you that you can't take what belongs to me without paying me for it. I'll hit you with my stick! (He strikes the rock with his stick.)

I'll hit you again! You still won't say anything? You still won't give me my money? I'll push you and pull you and throw you over. (He pushes the rock a little way.)

There! I have pushed you away from where you were sitting. What's this? Pieces of gold? (He picks up some pieces of gold that were half-buried under the rock.) So that's where your money was! You have been sitting on it.

Well, I shall take this money. It will pay for the butter you took from me. I promised Mother I would get the money from you. Now I have it.

Good day to you, Friend Town. Don't ever again try to keep something that belongs to somebody else.

Scene 5

Time: A short time later

Place: The farmhouse kitchen

(Manwick's mother is sewing.)

MOTHER: Well, Manwick, you are back very soon. Did you have the luck to get your money for the butter?

MANWICK: Yes, Mother. I have the money. Here it is. Look! I told you I would bring back plenty of money.

MOTHER: Gold pieces! Is it possible? I can hardly believe my eyes! Where did you get all this gold?

MANWICK: From the town, Mother. That's the money for the butter.

MOTHER: I don't understand your talk. Just how did you get this gold from the town?

MANWICK: I went back and asked the town to pay me for the butter. But the town would not say a word. It would not say yes, and it would not say no.

That made me angry. So I hit it with my stick, and then I pushed it over on its side. And there, partly buried under it, were the gold pieces. This money is really ours for the butter.

MOTHER: I don't understand, Manwick. I don't understand it at all. It sounds to me as if you found money which some bad men put under a rock to get it out of sight until they can come back for it.

I'll keep it while I try to find out who lost it. If nobody asks for it, then the gold will belong to us. Think of having so much gold!

MANWICK: Do you need anything else done in town, Mother?

MOTHER: Well, I do have some meat that I would like to sell in town. But I know I can't trust you to do that.

MANWICK: Why not? Didn't I bring back all these gold pieces for your butter just as I promised I would?

MOTHER: Yes, but I'm not sure whether we may keep and use this money. It doesn't belong to us yet.

MANWICK: Oh, please let me go to town for you again, Mother! I'll be sure to get plenty of money for the meat. I got a lot of money for the butter.

MOTHER: I don't know what to say. I have so much work to do that I can't go myself, and there isn't anyone else to send. I guess I'll have to let you go. But a town is not a big rock, Manwick. People live in a town.

MANWICK: Oh! I didn't know that, Mother. Now I will find the town without any trouble at all.

MOTHER: I hope you will. Now I'll put my sewing away and we'll have dinner. This afternoon you must try to do more work in the cornfield. You are not much good as a farmer, Manwick.

Time: The next day

Place: The main street of the town

(Manwick walks slowly along, looking at the store windows. Many persons pass him, but he does not talk to them. Soon some dogs smell the meat he is carrying in a bundle under his arm and start barking. Manwick stops.)

MANWICK: Good morning, friends. Would you like to buy some of my meat? (The dogs bark after every question.) You would? How about a little piece first, just to taste it? Here you are. It's good, isn't it? (The dogs eat the meat and leap up teasing for more.)

You like it and want some more? There! And here's another piece. And another bigger piece this time. What, you want still more? You've eaten all the meat. There is no more left.

Pay me for it now, please. Which one of you will pay for it? (The dogs start running away.) You're all running away. Oh, no, you won't. That's no way to act. The best-looking dog must belong to the person with the most money. That dog shall pay me for my meat.

(Manwick catches a dog. The dog barks.) I've got you! Pay me for the meat, or I'll take you to the King, and I'll tell him you took my meat without paying for it.

You won't give me my money? Very well! You're going to the King with me right now. (Manwick walks off with the barking dog.)

Scene 7

Time: A few minutes later

Place: Outside the King's room

(One footman stands at each side of the door to the room. Manwick walks up to the first footman, with the dog by his side. The dog barks once in a while.)

FIRST FOOTMAN: Stop! Who goes there?

MANWICK: I am Manwick. I must see the King.

FIRST FOOTMAN: Not everybody may get in to see the King. You have to have a good reason. What do you want to see him about?

MANWICK: Somebody took something from me without paying me. I must tell the King about it. He must see that I get my money.

SECOND FOOTMAN: That is a good reason for wanting to see the King. The King is a good man. He will not let anyone take things without paying for them.

FIRST FOOTMAN: I'll let you pass inside to see the King. But first you must promise me something.

MANWICK: What do you want me to promise?

FIRST FOOTMAN: You must promise to give me half of what you receive from the King.

MANWICK: I promise.

SECOND FOOTMAN: You must also promise me half of what you receive from the King, or else I will not let you pass.

MANWICK: I promise to give you, too, half of what I receive from the King. Now let me go into the King's room.

FIRST FOOTMAN: You may pass inside, Manwick. Leave the dog with us.

(Manwick goes in through the door. The footmen laugh.)

SECOND FOOTMAN: How is it possible for that Manwick to be so silly? If he gives each of us half of what he receives from the King, we'll have it all for ourselves. He'll have nothing for himself.

Scene 8

Time: A few minutes later

Place: A large room in the palace

(The King sits in a high, golden chair. The Princess sits in a smaller golden chair at his side. The Princess looks sad and does not smile. Men and women in fine clothes stand around the chairs of the King and the Princess. Manwick walks up to the King and bows.)

KING: Well, young man, why are you here?

MANWICK: Somebody has taken something from me without paying me, your Majesty.

KING: That must never happen in my land! Tell me how it happened, and I shall see that you get your money.

MANWICK: My name is Manwick, your Majesty. My mother and I live by ourselves on a farm and I've never been to town before. I brought a bundle of meat to sell. I walked along the streets, looking at all the people and the houses.

KING: Everything must have seemed strange to you.

MANWICK: Very strange, your Majesty. Soon
I saw that many dogs were following me.

KING: Well, you were carrying a bundle of
meat, you say. The dogs must have smelled
the meat.

MANWICK: That's right, your Majesty. The
dogs must have smelled the meat. So I
thought to myself, if the dogs like the smell
of the meat so much, they will surely like
to eat the meat. So I gave them little
pieces to taste.

KING: That was very kind of you. You must
like animals. Go on with your story.

MANWICK: I do like animals, your Majesty.
Well, I kept giving the dogs little pieces
of the meat, and before I knew it they
had eaten all the meat I had brought to
town.

KING: But why did you do that, Manwick? Why did you give them all your meat? You wanted to sell it.

MANWICK: But the dogs ate the meat, so I was sure they wanted it. They ate the meat, so I think they should pay for it.

KING: You think the dogs should pay for the meat?

MANWICK: Yes, your Majesty. Why not? But they didn't pay. They ran away. I want you to help me get my money from the dogs who took my meat.

KING: (Laughs) Well! I never heard of anything like this in all my days!

PRINCESS: (Laughs) Oh, Father! I never heard anything so funny! He thinks the dogs should pay him! (The Princess laughs a long time.)

KING: (Surprised) My dear daughter! You're laughing for the first time in your life. This young man has made you laugh.

Manwick, I have promised that the person who makes the Princess laugh shall have her for his wife. You are the lucky man who has done that. You shall have the Princess for your wife.

MANWICK: But I don't want the Princess for my wife, your Majesty.

KING: What's that? You don't want the Princess?

MANWICK: No, your Majesty.

KING: Well, I must say I am surprised at that! How unusual that a young man should refuse to have a pretty girl like the Princess for his wife!

But, you have made the Princess laugh, Manwick. You must have something fine for doing that. I'll give you a bag of one hundred gold pieces.

MANWICK: No, thank you. I don't want a bag of gold.

KING: That's even more unusual! You refused the Princess, and now you refuse the hundred pieces of gold. What do you want, Manwick?

MANWICK: I want to be hit with a stick one hundred times.

KING: That's the very strangest wish I've ever heard! When he can have the Princess or a bag of gold, he asks for one hundred blows with a stick! Aren't you making a mistake, Manwick? Is that what you really want?

MANWICK: It's no mistake, your Majesty. That's what I really want.

KING: Then you shall have your wish. You shall be taken out immediately and get one hundred blows with a stick.

MANWICK: Wait! Don't give the blows to me, your Majesty. Give half of them to each of the footmen outside your door.

KING: But why should the footmen get the blows of the stick?

MANWICK: Because, your Majesty, each one of the footmen made me promise to give him half of what I received from you. I had to promise that before they would let me into this room to talk to you. And so I want each one of them to get half of the one hundred blows with the stick.

KING: (Laughs loudly) I shall see that your promise is kept. Those footmen shall have your one hundred blows with the stick. They had no right to ask anything for letting you come in here. Any man in my land may come and talk to me.

As for you, Manwick, you are more clever than you seem. Are you sure you don't really want the Princess for your wife?

MANWICK: Now that I have kept my promise to the footmen, your Majesty, I have a different wish. Now I should like very much to have the Princess, if she will have me.

PRINCESS: I like you, Manwick. I like the way you handled the footmen. With a good teacher, you could become very clever. Best of all, you have made me laugh, and I am sure I shall find happiness as your wife.

KING: We'll send for your mother to come and live with us in the palace, Manwick. We'll all live happily together, and everybody will be glad that you went to town!

You know that sometimes there are silent letters in words. For example, the **k** in **know, knock,** and **knew** is silent. Whenever you see **kn** at the beginning of a word, you will know that only the **n** is sounded.

Think how you would say the words in very black letters in the following sentences:

I am learning to tie a square **knot.**

A **knitting** needle is not like a sewing needle.

A good **knife** cuts well.

Turn the **knob,** and the door will open.

The **w** in **write** and **wrong** is silent. When you see **wr** at the beginning of a word, remember that only the **r** is sounded.

Think how you would say the words in very black letters in these sentences:

Tom **wrote** to Dick about the train **wreck.**

I'll **wrap** up the stockings with the coat.

The mittens cover his hands and **wrists.**

He took the pipe apart with a big **wrench.**

You know about silent **e** on the end of a word. Sometimes there is a silent **b** on the end of a word. Say the words **lamb** and **climb** softly to yourself. You can hear the sound of **m,** but the **b** is silent.

Think how you would say the words in very black letters in these sentences:

The storm broke a **limb** off the tree.

Comb your hair and come down for dinner, or there won't be a **crumb** left.

Sometimes there is a silent **t** in a word. Say the words **often, listen,** and **whistle** to yourself. Notice that the **t** is silent.

Think how you would say the words in very black letters in these sentences:

Fasten the gate so the cows won't get out.

When something shines, we say that it **glistens.**

A few words have a silent **u** in them. Say the word **guess** to yourself, for example. You cannot hear the sound of the **u**.

Think how you would say the word in very black letters in this sentence:

A **guest** is a person who comes to visit.

What Does It Mean?

Read the following sentence: The road ran along the edge of the lake. Does the sentence mean that the road hurried along the edge of the lake? No, it means that the road had been built along the edge of the lake.

Now read each of the following numbered sentences and think what the words in very black letters mean. Then help your class decide on the answer to each question.

1. When the little boy saw the big balloon bouncing along, **his eyes nearly popped out of his head.** Did the boy's eyes nearly jump out of his head, or was the boy just very greatly surprised?

2. Dot's mother said, **"Keep an eye on the clock,** or you'll be late for school." Did she mean that Dot should hold one eye against the clock, or did she mean that Dot should watch the clock so as to know when to leave for school?

3. Mary **dropped her eyes** when the teacher spoke to her. Did Mary's eyes fall on the floor, or did she just look down?

310

Help your class decide what the words printed in very black letters mean in each of the following numbered sentences:

4. Mother said, "**Be on the watch** for a mitten among those stockings as you put them away, Jane."

5. "We'll **make some money** this week with our fruits and peanuts at the country fair," said Tom.

6. In the early days of our country the farmers had to **keep an eye out** for the Indians.

7. When Bill fell into the river, he **lost his head** immediately and nearly drowned.

8. The **stretch of road** between the river and the lake **winds** among steep hills.

9. The sun **broke through** the clouds, and the rain stopped pouring down.

10. If Dick had not **caught sight of** the smoke, something much worse would have happened.

11. John Hill is a boy who always **keeps his promises.**

12. Jack **stood up** for his friends.

Sense, Sound, and Syllables

Here are three ways to help yourself find out what a strange word is in your reading:

1. Use your good sense and the sound that the strange word begins with.

2. If the word ends with a syllable such as **ed, er, en, est,** or **ing,** notice what the word would be if the ending were left off.

3. Try to see what syllables make up the word. Say the word by syllables.

In the following story the words printed in very black letters may be strange to you. Use the three ways of helping yourself read those words.

The Horse That Liked Music

Long before the sun **streamed** through the window, Dan was out of bed and completely **dressed.** Today was the day of the parade!

"Hurry, Dan!" his mother called. "You must eat and do your **chores**. You've no time to lose if you want to see your school's **float** in the parade!"

When Dan was on his way to the barn, his mother called, "Pay attention to your work so that you'll finish in time. And don't play your **bagpipes** today."

Dan's grandfather had given him some bagpipes. Each day when Dan had finished his chores, he would play them for **Prancer**, his pet horse.

He liked **playing** for Prancer. His friends would tease him when he didn't play well. But no matter how he played, Prancer never teased him.

How Prancer liked music! He would dance and **toss** his head back and forth as soon as Dan would begin to play.

Dan **finished** his work **quickly** that morning. By the time he was dressed for the parade, his mother and father were in the wagon ready to go. Prancer was waiting by the wagon.

"May I ride Prancer to town?" Dan asked.

"No, Dan," his father **answered**. "We must leave him at home. He'll just be a bother. There won't be a place for him in town today."

Dan was less happy than before. He went up to Prancer and spoke to him **softly**, "I'll play the bagpipes for you when I come back, Prancer."

Dan **watched** Prancer until the wagon went over a hill and Prancer had completely disappeared from sight.

At last they were in the town. Dan, his mother, and his father **climbed** out of the wagon and stood on the street waiting for the parade to begin.

Soon the band began to play. Dan could hear the bagpipe music as the band **marched smartly** down the street. The Highland School float was behind the band. Two horses pulled it. How beautiful it was!

Dan opened his eyes wide. There was another horse in front of the float, dancing to the music of the band. It was Prancer!

In a flash, Dan was in the street and had **grabbed** the rope that hung from Prancer's neck. Just as Dan was about to pull him out of the parade, Prancer danced and tossed his head back and forth.

"It's a trick horse!" someone shouted.

"There's a dancing horse!" a little girl **exclaimed**. People began to **clap** loudly.

"Could they be **clapping** for Prancer?" Dan thought. "Who could ever have imagined such a thing!"

Just then Dan heard a boy cry, "Let's follow the trick horse!"

Dan was as happy as ever he had been. He held **tightly** to the rope as Prancer danced to the music and tossed his head back and forth.

Down one street and up another they went until they reached the square. Prancer was the **star** of the parade!

Then the music stopped. On a platform stood a **tall** man. All attention was fixed on him.

The tall man said, "First prize goes to Highland School for the trick horse that led the float!"

All the way home, Dan kept turning around to look at Prancer. Just as though the band were still playing, Prancer kept dancing as he **trotted** along behind the wagon.

VOCABULARY

LOOKING AHEAD, the first book for the third year, is planned to follow the second book for the second year, ON WE GO. It repeats each word in the vocabulary of ON WE GO, except some proper names. The names of characters in LOOKING AHEAD are not counted as new words unless the names are also used as meaningful words. The following list contains the 378 new words introduced in LOOKING AHEAD. Variants formed by adding *n, en, s, es, d, ed; ing, er, est, y, ly,* or *ful,* or the prefix *un,* to words previously taught, and compounds formed by joining two word forms previously taught are not counted as new words. Contractions ending in *n't, 've, 'd, 'll,* or *'re* are not counted as new words after the special exercises in which their formation is taught. The list does not include words which are used for practice in the special lessons for developing the power to unlock words independently.

5. desk	26. plenty	43. you've	few
6. ——	busy	44. squawking	61. sales
7. ——	vacation	bought	62. change
8. ——	27. dairy	45. winter	except
9. ——	week	46. we've	63. daughter
10. grandfather	sun	47. blossoms	nice
wood	28. clanged	peach	miles
11. ——	tracks	48. pick	64. certainly
12. ——	29. seat	sister	present
13. ——	excited	49. cost	set
14. ——	30. you're	less	65. ——
15. ——	31. we're	50. branch	66. extra
16. ——	32. chicken	lot	67. ——
17. ——	cooked	51. bright	68. feather
18. trolley	problems	dropped	sentence
family	33. ought	52. yet	69. ——
job	wouldn't	53. able	70. books
19. drove	34. suddenly	easy	mark
early	platform	sticks	write
since	stove	54. hang	71. ——
20. worry	35. nails	ripe	72. ——
matter	motorman	they'll	73. ——
already	stool	55. basket	74. ——
21. cup	36. shelf	beautiful	75. ——
coffee	furniture	spend	76. ourselves
move	37. stalls	56. toward	77. ——
22. buses	rooster	57. beyond	78. ——
drive	grass	reach	79. ——
rent	38. cherry	sorry	80. ——
23. company	gathered	58. against	81. ——
month	39. instead	perhaps	82. ——
pay	bicycle	sad	83. ——
24. power	40. groceries	59. chance	84. ——
hitch	corner	fall	85. ——
25. porch	41. felt	saving	86. ——
farther	42. ——	60. during	87. ——

317

88. ——
89. ——
90. woke
91. ——
92. ——
93. ——
94. ——
95. ——
96. ——
97. ——
98. ——
99. fair
ribbons
women
100. fruits
pies
vegetables
101. ——
102. warm
wind
103. probably
safely
104. bent
pen
close
105. refuses
softly
106. held
smart
107. fix
great
Midnight
108. butt
shadow
wonderful
109. candy
train
110. decide
wildly
111. chase
leaped
112. plan
113. cash
state
114. indeed
won
115. proudly
shining
116. grape
jelly
sweet

117. eagerly
118. clippers
special
wool
119. square
tight
120. acting
arrived
bundle
121. though
122. crowded
123. ——
124. expected
125. ——
126. ——
127. agree
128. ——
129. ——
130. notice
whether
131. ——
132. hound
Ranger
Tennessee
133. country
crack
travel
134. free
lend
quite
135. finally
spoke
136. bugs
potato
137. idea
mule
suppose
138. ——
139. ——
140. course
pack
peddler
141. ——
142. ——
143. interesting
144. heavy
leaning
145. hundred
least
nodded
146. Boston

ocean
trudged
147. cousin
imagine
visit
148. empty
half
supper
149. salt
scolded
silver
150. heart
scratch
voice
151. appeared
152. hay
lay
yard
153. flashed
154. pile
sir
155. Doctor
replied
serious
156. clear
157. enjoy
lifted
158. meal
meet
trade
159. cheerfully
160. length
needles
spices
161. anxiously
chose
events
162. inn
several
life
163. afternoon
Patch
Point
164. brought
exclaimed
shop
165. explained
trip
166. ——
167. especially
important

168. happiness
169. realizes
shook
170. speaking
straight
171. rain
stormy
172. neighbor
raising
173. ——
174. age
stone
175. ——
176. ——
177. ——
178. ——
179. ——
180. ——
181. ——
182. correctly
vowel
183. ——
184. syllables
185. ——
186. ——
187. ——
188. either
189. ——
190. danger
rocks
ships
191. lakes
shores
built
192. harbors
lamp
warn
193. oil
wick
194. fog
foghorn
195. ——
196. ——
197. ——
198. ——
199. ——
200. ——
201. ——
202. ——
203. ——
204. ——

205. ——
206. ——
207. ——
208. ——
209. ——
210. ——
211. ——
212. ——
213. heels
toes
copper
214. born
godmother
215. gift
leather
wander
216. behaved
habit
wore
217. pinch
218. cowslips
marsh
weather
219. path
steep
threw
220. edge
insisted
mud
221. among
comfortable
delight
222. stockings
223. Dr.
received
teased
224. attention
examples
master
225. ashamed
class
226. lose
227. clock

strike
trust
228. borrow
229. Main
230. partner
possible
reason
231. discovered
minutes
232. direction
leading
lost
233. buried
234. completely
thick
walls
235. bear
worse
236. coat
disappeared
237. ——
238. ——
239. ——
240. ——
241. ——
242. ——
243. ——
244. ——
245. ——
246. bothered
247. frame
hung
rang
248. continued
King
teeth
249. ding
dong
roof
250. ——
251. mistake
ordered
rushed

252. sight
unless
253. ——
254. rid
255. hour
256. barking
257. pour
smoke
258. alarm
flames
spreading
259. ——
260. usual
261. ——
262. ——
263. ——
264. rich
servants
umbrellas
265. blocks
mountain
266. ah
palace
267. immedi-
ately
prince
268. dry
Majesty
earth
269. cloud
rivers
270. ——
271. ——
272. barbecue
Fox
Wolf
273. corn
roast
tastes
274. bit
forth
sick
275. forks

276. ——
277. meat
278. ——
279. ——
280. ——
281. ——
282. ——
283. ——
284. scenes
person
285. ——
286. ——
287. ——
288. ——
289. ——
290. ——
291. ——
292. ——
293. ——
294. ——
295. ——
296. ——
297. ——
298. ——
299. ——
300. ——
301. ——
302. ——
303. ——
304. ——
305. ——
306. ——
307. ——
308. ——
309. ——
310. ——
311. ——
312. ——
313. ——
314. ——
315. ——
316. ——

ACKNOWLEDGMENTS

Grateful acknowledgment is made to the following publishers and authors for permission to adapt and use copyrighted material:

To William Morrow and Company, Inc. for "Eddie and the Desk" adapted from *Little Eddie* by Carolyn Haywood, copyright, 1947 by William Morrow and Company, Inc., by permission of William Morrow and Company, Inc.

To David McKay Company for permission to adapt the story *The Trolley Car Family* by Eleanor Clymer.

To Story Parade, Inc. for permission to adapt the following stories: "The Bicycle Tree" by Mildred Lawrence, copyright, 1947 and "Presents for Mother" by Robin Palmer, copyright, 1947.

To Harper & Brothers for permission to use the poem "Merry-Go-Round" from *I Like Machinery* by Dorothy Baruch.

To Expression Company for permission to use the poem "When I Go Fishing" from the book *Better Speech and Better Reading.*

To John C. Winston Company for permission to adapt the story *Midnight and Jeremiah* by Sterling North.

To Ada Campbell Rose for permission to adapt her story "Young Tennessee and Old Man Blowdy."

To Electa Clark for permission to adapt her story "Nathan and the Peddler."

To Mary E. Anthony for permission to adapt her story "The Story of a Brave Girl."

To The Macmillan Company for permission to adapt the story "Timothy's Shoes" from the book of the same name by Juliana Horatio Ewing, copyright, 1922.

To Helen Fuller Orton for permission to adapt her story "The Dinner Bell."

The play "Manwick Goes to Town" is a Danish folk tale adapted especially for this book by Fan Kissen.

The illustrations for "The Trolley Car Family" were made by Katherine Sampson; for page 3, and "The Bicycle Tree" by Albert D. and Violet Jousset; those for pages 1, 4, "Presents for Mother," pages 98–101, "Jeremiah's Black Lamb, pages 190–195, and "Sally Finds a Way" by Mary Stevens; those for "Young Tennessee and Old Sam," pages 140 and 142, and "Nathan and the Peddler" by C. L. Hartman; those for page 212, "Eddie and the Desk," and "The Magic Shoes" by Violet Lamont; those for "The Dinner Bell," page 264, "The Stonecutter," "Brother Fox and the Barbecues," and "Manwick Goes to Town" by Bruno Frost; those for pages 97 and 211 by Marguerite K. Scott; those for pages 94–95, 188–189, and 282–283 by Hertha Depper; and those for pages 312, 314, and 315 by Beth Krush.